The New
Wider World
Second Edition COURSEMATE

for IGCSE Geography

John Edwards

Skills unit developed by
Simon Ross

Nelson Thornes

Contents

Introduction

About this book

This New Wider World Coursemate matches the content of *The New Wider World* to your own GCSE/Standard Grade Geography specification, and follows the same order. It is a pocket companion for your course and provides a summary of the core information you will need to know and revise for your GCSE/Standard Grade Geography examinations.

How the specification is structured

The specification is divided into three themes, which are collectively designed to develop an understanding of both the natural and human environments:

Theme 1:   Population and Settlement
Theme 2:   The Natural Environment
Theme 3:   Economic Development and the Use of Resources.

How the specification is assessed

All candidates take Paper 1, Paper 2, and *either* Paper 3 *or* Paper 4.
Paper 1 (1 hour 45 minutes) (75 marks)
Candidates will be required to answer three questions. Six questions are set, two on each of the three themes.
Paper 2 (1 hour 30 minutes) (60 marks)
This paper is mainly skills based, and does not require specific knowledge of places. Candidates must answer all questions, one of which will be based on a topographical map.
Paper 3 Coursework (60 marks)
This school-based assignment will be set by the teacher. It must comprise 1200–1500 words.
Paper 4 Alternative to coursework (1 hour 30 minutes) (60 marks)
Candidates are set a series of tasks on issues relating to one or more of the specification themes. Candidates must answer all questions. Questions will test data collection skills, for example questionnaire and measurement techniques.

How your Coursemate is organised

Your Coursemate follows the same structure and order as the topics in your specification. Most of the information is from *The New Wider World*, so your book acts as a companion to both *The New Wider World* and your own specification. Your Coursemate is organised in the following way:

- The **Unit/Theme** and **chapter headings** match those used in the specification.
- The **page references** to *The New Wider World* at the beginning of each chapter tell you which pages in the textbook your Coursemate refers to.
- The **Key Questions** relate to those which appear in your specification, and the content of your Coursemate is organised around these.

- **Key words to know** – these are the key geographical words and terms you need to know and be able to use.
- **Check this!...** – doing these questions will check that you know and understand the key concepts in each chapter.
- **Back to...** is a cross-reference to *The New Wider World* for finding more information. It can also be a cross-reference to other information in your Coursemate.
- **Case Studies** are based on the Case Studies and Place Studies in *The New Wider World*, and **Case Study Extras** are new case studies written especially for your specification. Where relevant these will: refer you back to the textbook for more information; tell you how to get the best from your case study; provide links to other topics; provide updates to the case study which may be websites accessed via a link to the Nelson Thornes website at: www.nelsonthornes.com/newwiderworld *and* include questions which encourage you to learn the case study so that you can use it well in your examination.
- **Exam practice** – these questions are similar to those you will meet in the examination. You can check your answers by going to *The New Wider World* website at: www.nelsonthornes.com/newwiderworld.
- Each **Exam Practice** question is followed by **Exam Tips** to provide help and advice on answering the question.

At the end of this book you will find a chapter on **geographical skills**. This gives information on the basic geographical skills you will need for the interpretation, presentation and analysis of geographical information and data throughout your Geography course and in your examinations.

> All references to *The New Wider World* in your Coursemate are to the Second Edition.

1 How fast is the world's population growing? What are the causes and consequences of overpopulation and underpopulation?

Population trends

The annual growth rate of the world's population rose slowly but steadily until the beginning of the nineteenth century. For the next 150 years it grew at an increasingly faster rate. This process is called a **population explosion**. During the 1960s and 1970s the world's population grew, on average, by a record 2 per cent per year (Figure 1.1). This growth rate caused increasing concern. It was even higher in the **less economically developed countries (LEDCs)**.

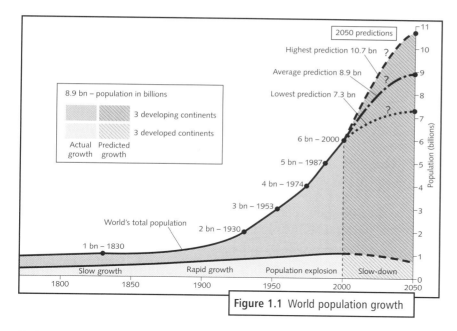

Figure 1.1 World population growth

1 Population dynamics

KEY QUESTIONS

1 How fast is the world's population growing? What are the causes and consequences of overpopulation and underpopulation?

2 What are the reasons for contrasting patterns of population change?

3 What are the consequences of different patterns of population growth?

4 What are the reasons for different types of population structure?

5 What factors influence the density and distribution of population and population migration?

Key words to know

Population explosion
Less economically developed countries (LEDCs)
Birth rate

Estimates suggested that the world's population of 3039 million in 1960 would reach 7600 million by the end of the century and 11 000 million by 2050.

In October 1999 the United Nations (UN) claimed that the growth rate had fallen to 1.6 per cent per year, and was likely to drop to 1.0 per cent by 2015 and to 0.5 per cent by 2050. According to the UN, in October 1999 the world's population reached 6000 million (6 billion) – well below the predicted 7600 million (7.6 billion).

Even so, it is still growing by 140 persons per minute, which is 78 million each year.

People across most of the world are living longer. So why is the annual growth rate slowing down? This is due to a combination of factors, which include:

- a faster than predicted decline in the **birth rate** across the world

Key words to know

Fertility rate
Life expectancy

Back to ...

The New Wider World
pp14–15 for reasons why
life expectancy is increasing.

- improvements in family planning, basic education and female literacy, which have all led to smaller families (that is, a lower **fertility rate**)
- the one-child policy in China, a country with over 20 per cent of the world's population
- diseases such as AIDS and malaria which reduce **life expectancy**, especially in sub-Saharan countries in Africa which have the world's highest birth rates.

These population figures need to be treated carefully, as they can only be an estimation. This is because census data for most countries is only collected every ten years (and for some countries even less). Also, many people may not return forms or complete them accurately, while groups of people like refugees, illegal immigrants and shanty-town dwellers may be excluded or missed.

Check this!...

1 Describe the pattern of population growth shown on Figure 1.1.

2 What is meant by the term 'population explosion'?

3 Explain why the rate of increase in population has slowed down in recent years.

Population growth

Population change depends mainly on the balance between the birth rate and the death rate. It is also, but to a lesser extent, affected by **migration**.

The birth rate is the average number of live births in a year for every 1000 people in the total population. The **death rate** is the average number of deaths per 1000 people in the population. The difference between the birth rate and the death rate is either the **natural increase** (where the birth rate is the higher) or the **natural decrease** (where the death rate is the higher).

Throughout history the world's population, and that of individual countries, has usually shown a natural increase. There have been exceptions, though:

Key words to know

Migration
Death rate
Natural increase
Natural decrease

Back to ...

The New Wider World **p13** for
information on China's
one-child policy.

- during times of disease – the bubonic plague that spread across the world in the Middle Ages, and AIDS in present-day Africa
- as a result of war – western Europe during the two World Wars and more recently in Iraq
- due to recent improvements in family planning and female education – either voluntary as in Australia and New Zealand, or enforced as with China's one-child policy.

AIDS in Botswana

Until recently Botswana was known as the country with the highest rate of HIV/AIDS in the world. In 2004, it was estimated that 300 000 people in Botswana were HIV positive, with nearly 40% of the 15–49 age group infected. As a result, life expectancy is likely to drop from 67 to 47 years by 2010, with a serious negative effect on the economy of the country.

In response to the growing crisis, the Botswana government has become the first country in Africa to introduce widespread anti-AIDS drugs through its public health system, under a programme named 'Masa', which means 'new dawn'. Free drugs and counselling are provided in four priority areas, including the capital Gaborone. People initially targeted include all those with AIDS-related illnesses, pregnant women, and children older than six months. The scheme cost the government over $30 million in its first year – on average nearly $10 000 per patient.

Despite the existence of Masa, people in Botswana are still reluctant to know their HIV status. According to official estimates, 110 000 people are eligible for treatment, yet only 5000 are actually on treatment.

Using your case study

Use this case study to answer questions on population dynamics. You should:
- understand the impact that HIV/AIDS has had on life expectancy and the economy in Botswana
- know about the government's response to the crisis
- explain why people have been reluctant to take part in testing for HIV/AIDS.

Update

Go to *The NWW Coursemates* website for a link to a UN news and humanitarian news and information service which contains updated material about HIV/AIDS.

Learn it!

1 What impact has AIDS had on life expectancy in Botswana?

2 What has the government done about the crisis?

3 Why do you think some people in Botswana have been reluctant to be tested for HIV/AIDS?

The demographic transition model

The **demographic transition model** shows the relationship between birth rates and death rates. It describes how, over time, population growth rates change (Figure 1.2 on page 4). The model, which was based on population changes in several industrialised countries in western Europe and North America, suggested that there were four stages through which *all* countries will eventually pass.

A **model** is a simplification of something that is complicated. The demographic transition model has some limitations. In this case it is the assumption that the sequence of population change results from an increase in industrialisation. Most **more economically developed countries (MEDCs)** have reached stage 4, but it is accepted that many of the LEDCs will never become industrialised. Although the more developed LEDCs have reached stage 3, most of the least developed countries remain at stage 2.

Key words to know

Demographic transition model
Model
More economically developed countries (MEDCs)

Back to ...

The New Wider World **p7**
Figure 1.6 for examples of birth and death rates at different stages of the demographic transition model.

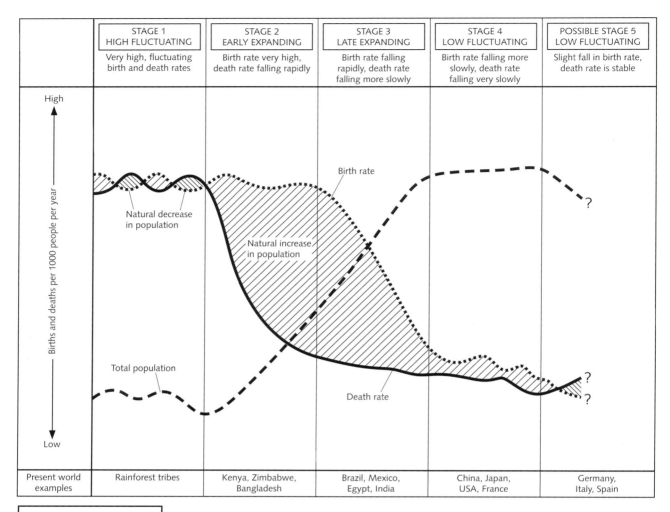

	STAGE 1 HIGH FLUCTUATING	STAGE 2 EARLY EXPANDING	STAGE 3 LATE EXPANDING	STAGE 4 LOW FLUCTUATING	POSSIBLE STAGE 5 LOW FLUCTUATING
	Very high, fluctuating birth and death rates	Birth rate very high, death rate falling rapidly	Birth rate falling rapidly, death rate falling more slowly	Birth rate falling more slowly, death rate falling very slowly	Slight fall in birth rate, death rate is stable
Present world examples	Rainforest tribes	Kenya, Zimbabwe, Bangladesh	Brazil, Mexico, Egypt, India	China, Japan, USA, France	Germany, Italy, Spain

Figure 1.2 The demographic transition model

Check this!...

1 What is meant by the terms 'birth rate', 'death rate' and 'natural increase'?

2 Explain why there could be a natural decrease in the population of a country.

3 Describe the main features of the demographic transition model.

4 Why can the model not be applied to all countries?

5 In which stage of the model is the country in which you live? Give reasons for your answer.

Since the 1990s several MEDCs appear to be entering a new, fifth stage. This is where the birth rate is beginning to fall below the death rate. It is predicted that if this trend continues, countries entering this stage will eventually see a decrease in their total population.

- **Overpopulation:** the resources cannot sustain the current population. As long as there is overpopulation the quality of life will decline through unemployment, pollution and degradation of the environment.
- **Underpopulation:** the population cannot fully use the resources available. Quality of life can only slowly be improved. An increase in population would lead to an increase in quality of life.
- **Optimum population:** the population is such that it can maximise the benefits from the resources available. It is only when we have optimum populationthat the quality of life is maximised.

On global and continental scales, patterns of population growth are mainly affected by physical factors such as relief, climate and natural resources. At regional and more local scales, patterns are more likely to be influenced by human factors. Some parts of the world are **overpopulated**, while others are **underpopulated**. However:

- For any place there are usually several reasons for population growth, e.g. the Nile Valley and Sahara Desert.

- Even within areas there are variations in population, e.g. parts of Japan are very crowded, yet less than one-fifth of the country is inhabited.
- The population of India is now more than 1 billion, and it is still increasing rapidly. During the twenty-first century India will become even more overpopulated, with resources being unable to sustain the population.
- Elsewhere in the world (mainly in MEDCs), population is in fact declining. In Bulgaria, for example, the population is set to decline by 40 per cent this century. There may also be overpopulation within countries, for example where people have migrated to cities for better jobs, housing, etc. (push factors). This has taken place in many LEDC cities. As the population of the world is so unevenly distributed, there are parts of the world that remain underpopulated, for example parts of Australia. Antarctica, while not home to a permanent population, has vast reserves of resources under its ice.

Figure 1.3 shows the factors affecting how the population of the world is distributed.

Key words to know

Overpopulation
Underpopulation
Optimum population

Figure 1.3 Factors affecting the distribution of the world's population

PHYSICAL

	Densely populated	Examples	Sparsely populated	Examples
Relief	Flat plains and low-lying undulating areas	Bangladesh	High, rugged mountains	Andes
	Broad river valleys	Ganges valley	Worn-down shield lands	Canadian Shield
	Foothills of active volcanoes	Etna, Pinatubo		
Climate	Evenly distributed rainfall with no temperature extremes	North-west Europe	Limited annual rainfall	Sahara Desert
	Areas with (i) high sunshine totals (ii) heavy snowfall for tourism	(i) Spanish costas (ii) Swiss alpine valleys	Low annual temperatures High annual humidity	Greenland Amazon rainforest
	Seasonal monsoon rainfall	Bangladesh	Unreliable seasonal rainfall	Sahel
Vegetation	Grasslands – easy to clear/farm	Paris basin	Forest	Amazonia, Canadian Shield
Soil	Deep fertile silt left by rivers	Nile valley and delta	Thin soils in mountainous or glaciated areas	Northern Scandinavia
	Volcanic soils	Etna	(i) lacking humus or (ii) affected by leaching	(i) Sahel (ii) rainforests
Natural resources	Minerals, e.g. coal, iron ore	Pennsylvania, Johannesburg	Lacking minerals	Ethiopia
	Energy supplies, e.g. HEP	Rhône valley	Lacking energy supplies	North-east Brazil
Water supply	Reliable supplies	North-west Europe	Unreliable supplies	Afghanistan
Natural routes	Gaps through mountains, confluence of valleys	Rhine valley, Paris	Mountain barrier	Himalayas

HUMAN

	Densely populated	Examples	Sparsely populated	Examples
Economic	Ports	New York, Sydney	Limited facilities for ports	Bangladesh
	Good roads, railways, airports	Germany, California	Poor transport links	Himalayas
	Industrial areas (traditional)	Pittsburgh, Ruhr	Lack of industrial development	Sudan
	Development of tourism	Banff (Canada), Jamaica	Lack of tourist developments	Iraq
	Money available for new high-tech industries	California, south of France	Lack of money for new investments	Nepal, Gaza
Political	Government investment	Tokyo region, north Italy	Lack of government investment	Dem. Rep. of the Congo
	New towns	Satellite towns around Cairo, Brasilia	Depopulation of rural and old industrial areas	North-east Brazil, Belgian coalfield
	Reclamation of land	Hong Kong Island, Dutch polders	Loss of land, e.g. deforestation, and soil erosion	Amazonia, Apennines, Sahel
Social	Better housing opportunities	Arizona	Poor housing opportunities	Afghanistan, Soweto
	Education, health facilities, entertainment	Sydney, Milan	Limited education, health facilities, entertainment	Rwanda

2 What are the reasons for contrasting patterns of population change?

Population change in developed and developing countries

Many of the LEDCs still fit into either stage 2 or stage 3 of the demographic transition model (see page 4). Most of the MEDCs have reached stage 4 (see page 4). This is because the LEDCs have a higher birth rate and a greater increase in their total population (Figure 1.4).

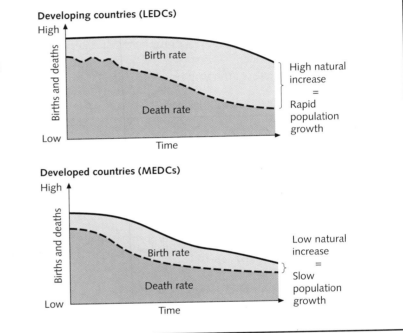

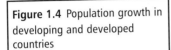
Figure 1.4 Population growth in developing and developed countries

Back to ...

Pages 3–4 of this *Coursemate* for a description of the demographic transition model; *The New Wider World* **p11** Figures 1.12 and 1.13 for graphs showing changes in world population between 1900 and 2050.

The growth and distribution of the world's population varies between continents:

- The continents with the fastest growth in population are the three developing ones of Africa, Asia and Latin America. Africa has the greatest growth despite its high death rate caused by AIDS, crop failure and civil war.
- The continents with the slowest growth rate are the three developed ones of Europe, North America and Australasia (Oceania). Estimates suggest that Europe is likely to show a population decrease by the middle of the twenty-first century.
- Most of the world's population live in Asia (approximately 40 per cent in China and India). In 1950, 76 per cent of the total lived in the three developing continents. This proportion had risen to 82 per cent by 2000 and is estimated to reach 88 per cent by 2050.

Check this!...

1 Which parts of the world have the fastest rates of population increase? Why do you think this is?

2 Which parts of the world have the slowest population growth rates? Explain your answer.

3 Describe and explain the rate of population change in the country in which you live.

Case Study

Population in Brazil

Back to ...

The New Wider World **pp16–17** for this case study of Brazil's population.

Using your case study

Use this case study to answer questions on population dynamics. You should:

- describe the distribution of Brazil's population
- explain why some parts of the country are densely populated, and some are sparsely populated
- describe and explain the structure of Brazil's population
- describe how the population of Brazil is changing.

Case study links

You may be able to use this case study for any aspect of a question on population dynamics.

Update

Go to *The NWW Coursemates* website for a link to 'Nation by Nation', which gives detailed country profiles, including information on population growth in Brazil.

Learn it!

1 Draw a simple sketch map to show the distribution of population in Brazil.

2 Explain why the population density is higher in some parts of the country than others.

3 Which stage of the demographic transition model do you think Brazil is in? Give reasons for your answer.

4 How is the population of Brazil changing?

3 What are the consequences of different patterns of population growth?

Changing population structures

Different patterns of population growth lead to varying population sizes, and also to variations in the number of young and old people. There are both problems and benefits for countries when there are large numbers of people under 15 or aged over 65. People in these age groups are known as **dependents**.

Key word to know

Dependents

Many under 15s ...

Countries at stages 2 and 3 of the demographic transition model are less economically developed and have a higher birth rate than those at stage 4. A high birth rate results in a large proportion of the total population being aged 15 or under. In Africa and much of southern Asia, this proportion is likely to be over 40 per cent and in Latin America over 30 per cent (in the MEDCs it is often under 20 per cent). This means that:

- at present, the large youthful population needs child health care and education – two services that these countries can ill afford
- in the future, there will be more people reaching child-bearing age.

Few under 15s ...

In contrast, several MEDCs are approaching stage 5 in the demographic transition model. Here the problem is becoming 'too few' children. This is because, in countries like Germany, Italy and Spain (together with China and its one-child policy), birth rates are at, or below, death rates.

This means that the **replacement rate**, which is when there are just enough children born to balance the number of people that die, is not being met. Countries where the replacement rate is not met face a decrease in their total population. For example, the population of Italy is predicted to fall from 56 million in 2000 to 41 million by 2050. The fear is that, in time, the country will:

- have too few consumers and skilled workers to keep their economy going
- have too few scientists and technicians to compete in the world market
- experience the closure of schools and shops, especially in smaller towns and villages
- face problems in providing for an ageing population.

People aged over 65 – an ageing population

There has been an increase in life expectancy (Figure 1.5) in MEDCs and more recently in some LEDCs. Life expectancy is the number of years that a person might be expected to live. It has increased due to:

- improved standards of hygiene and health education
- improvements in health care
- the development of new drugs and vaccines
- a better diet, both in quantity and quality
- advances in medical knowledge and techniques (some diseases and conditions which were untreatable can now be treated).

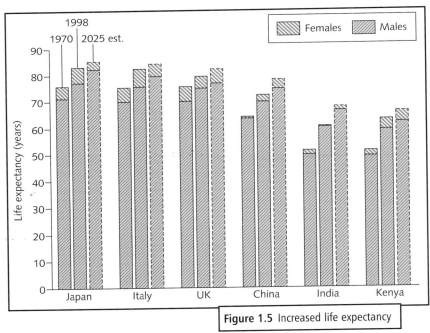

Figure 1.5 Increased life expectancy

The increase in life expectancy, together with a falling birth rate, means that an increasingly higher proportion of a country's population lives beyond 65 years, and even beyond 80. This process is referred to as **ageing**. By 2000, several MEDCs (Japan, and several countries in western Europe) had over 16 per cent of their population aged over 65. For the first time, they had more people aged over 65 than children aged under 15. The proportion of over-65s is predicted to rise to over 20 per cent by 2020 and, in some countries such as Japan and Italy, to reach 35 per cent by 2050. The consequences are likely to be a greater demand for the services needed by an elderly population. These will have to be paid for by a smaller proportion of people of working age. Figure 1.6 gives some of the problems created by an increasingly ageing population.

Back to ...

The New Wider World **p14**
Figure 1.18 which shows the percentage of population aged over 65 years, between 1950 and 2020.

Figure 1.6 Problems of an ageing population

A Problems created in a country ...	B Problems facing the elderly ...
An increasing amount of money is needed for the long-term care of the elderly.	Many have to live alone, especially women, when their partner dies.
An increasing amount of the family doctor's financial budget and time is taken up by the elderly.	There are long waits for hospital operations such as hip replacements.
There is an increase in long-term illnesses and those that make people house-bound, such as Parkinson's and Alzheimer's.	There are lengthy waits for hospital operations such as hip replacements.
There is an increasing dependence on a smaller group of economically active people to provide consumer goods and services as well as money through taxation.	Those who are still fit enough and willing to work often face bias and prejudice due to their age.
Less money is available for younger age groups, e.g. for education, improvements in transport or the provision of leisure and social amenities.	Those living in urban areas have a fear of crime and traffic; those in rural areas who cannot drive and where there is no public transport have difficulty getting to a doctor, hospital and shops.

Check this!...

1 What are some of the effects on a country of having a large proportion of the population aged under 15 years?

2 What is the replacement rate for a population? What might happen in a country if the replacement rate is not met?

3 What are the consequences for a country of having an ageing population?

4 What are the reasons for different types of population structure?

Population structures

The rate of natural increase, the birth rate, the death rate and life expectancy all affect the **population structure** of a country. The population structure can be shown by a **population pyramid**.

A population pyramid shows:
- the total population divided into five-year age groups, e.g. 5–9 years, 10–14 years
- the percentage of the total population, subdivided into males and females, in each of those groups.

The population pyramid for the United Kingdom, a typical MEDC, is shown in Figure 1.7. This graph shows:
- a 'rectangular' shape, indicating approximately the same number in each age group, a low death rate and a steady, or even a static, population growth

Key words to know

Population structure
Population pyramid

- a narrow base, indicating a low and falling birth rate
- that more boys are born than girls (a higher percentage of boys aged under 4 years)
- relatively large numbers aged 65 years and over, indicating a long life expectancy
- that more females than males live to over 65 years
- a relatively large proportion of the population in the pre- and post-reproductive age groups, and a relatively small number in the 15–64 age group, which is the one that produces children and most of the national wealth.

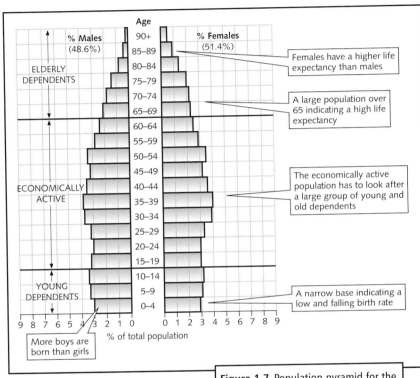

Figure 1.7 Population pyramid for the United Kingdom, an MEDC

Key words to know

Dependency ratio

This last feature can be shown as the **dependency ratio**:

$$\frac{\text{Non-economically active (children 0–14 plus elderly 65+)}}{\text{Economically active (those of working age 15–64)}} \times 100$$

Example: for UK 2001 (figures in millions):

$$\frac{11.105 + 9.341}{38.342} \times 100 = \text{dependency ratio of } 53.33$$

This means that for every 100 people of working age, there were 53.33 people dependent upon them.

Population pyramids enable comparisons to be made between countries, and can help a country to plan for future service needs such as hospitals if it has an ageing population, or fewer schools if it has a declining, younger population. Population pyramids include immigrants. There are four types of graph representing different stages of development, which are similar to the stages in the demographic transition model (Figure 1.8).

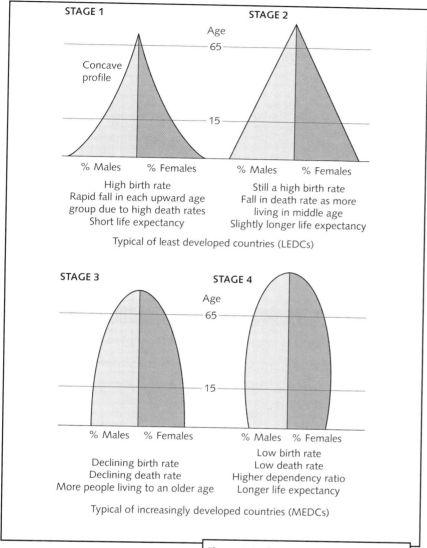

STAGE 1

Age
65

Concave profile

15

% Males   % Females

High birth rate
Rapid fall in each upward age group due to high death rates
Short life expectancy

STAGE 2

% Males   % Females

Still a high birth rate
Fall in death rate as more living in middle age
Slightly longer life expectancy

Typical of least developed countries (LEDCs)

STAGE 3

Age
65

15

% Males   % Females

Declining birth rate
Declining death rate
More people living to an older age

STAGE 4

% Males   % Females

Low birth rate
Low death rate
Higher dependency ratio
Longer life expectancy

Typical of increasingly developed countries (MEDCs)

Figure 1.8 Changing population structures

Stages of development

Three countries at different stages of economic development are Kenya, India and Japan. The most recent population pyramids for these countries are given in Figure 1.9. How well do you think the three pyramids fit with the models shown in Figure 1.8?

Kenya is the least wealthy of the three. Its wide base (0–4 years) confirms that it has the highest birth rate and that its population declines rapidly due to a high infant mortality rate. Birth and infant mortality rates in India, which is slightly more wealthy, are both declining. This is shown by the narrower base (0–4 years) and relatively more people reaching child-bearing age (20–24 years). Both countries, especially Kenya, have a rapidly narrowing pyramid. This indicates a high death rate and a short life expectancy (there are relatively few people aged over 65 years).

The pyramid for Japan shows a low birth rate, a low death rate, a low infant mortality rate and a long life expectancy. The graphs also

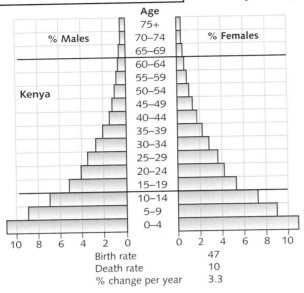

Figure 1.9 Population pyramids for Kenya, India and Japan, 2000

show that in Japan and India, as in most other countries, there are slightly more male than female births, but that females have the longer life expectancy.

Kenya

Birth rate 47
Death rate 10
% change per year 3.3

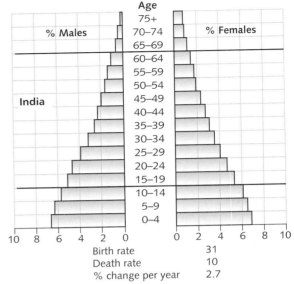

India

Birth rate 31
Death rate 10
% change per year 2.7

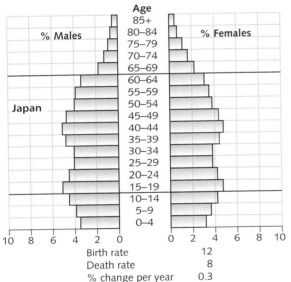

Japan

Birth rate 12
Death rate 8
% change per year 0.3

Check this!...

1 What is shown by a population pyramid?

2 What is meant by the term 'dependency ratio'?

3 Describe, using a simple diagram, the population structure of a typical MEDC.

4 How does this differ from the population structure in a typical LEDC?

5 Describe the population structure of the country in which you live, in terms of the information shown in Figure 1.8.

5 What factors influence the density and distribution of population and population migration?

Population distribution and density

Distribution describes the way in which people are spread across the Earth's surface. This distribution is uneven and changes over time. It is usual to show population distribution by a dot map (Figure 1.10). Notice how people are concentrated into certain parts of the world, making those places very crowded. At the same time, other areas have relatively few people living there. These are sparsely populated.

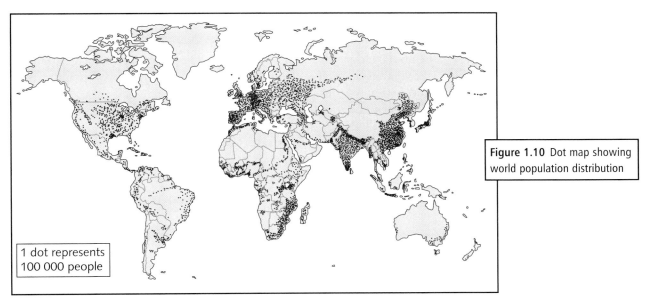

Figure 1.10 Dot map showing world population distribution

1 dot represents 100 000 people

Density describes the number of people living in a given area, usually a square kilometre (km^2). Density is found by dividing the total population of a place by its area. Population density is usually shown by a choropleth map (Figure 1.11). A choropleth map is easy to read as it shows generalisations, but it does tend to hide concentrations. For example:

- On Figure 1.11, Brazil appears to have a low population density. However, on a larger-scale map, several parts of the country are shown to have very high densities.
- Figure 1.11 suggests that the population of Egypt is evenly spread but in reality it is concentrated along the Nile Valley (Figure 1.10).

Key words to know

Population distribution
Population density

Back to ...

The New Wider World **p16**
Figure 1.23 for a detailed map showing the population of Brazil.
This *Coursemate* **p5** for reasons, with examples, why some parts of the world are densely populated while others are sparsely populated.

Figure 1.11 World population density by country

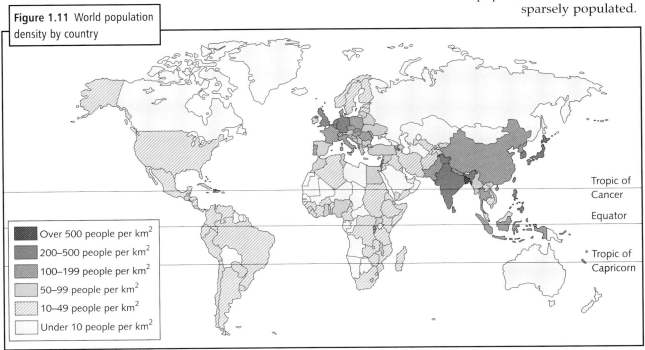

- Over 500 people per km^2
- 200–500 people per km^2
- 100–199 people per km^2
- 50–99 people per km^2
- 10–49 people per km^2
- Under 10 people per km^2

Tropic of Cancer

Equator

Tropic of Capricorn

Key words to know

Migration
Permanent international migration
Emigrants
Immigrants
Migration balance
Net migration loss
Net migration gain
Rural-to-urban migration
Voluntary migration
Forced migration

Migration

Migration is a movement and in human terms usually means a change of home. However, it can be applied to temporary, seasonal and daily movements as well as to permanent changes both between countries and within a country.

- **Permanent international migration** is the movement of people between countries.
- **Emigrants** are people who leave a country; **immigrants** are those who arrive in a country.
- The **migration balance** is the difference between the numbers of emigrants and immigrants.
- Countries with a **net migration loss** lose more people through emigration than they gain by immigration. Depending on the balance between their birth and death rates they may have a declining population.
- Countries with a **net migration gain** receive more people by immigration than they lose through emigration, and so will have an overall population increase.
- **Rural-to-urban migration**, the movement of people from the countryside to towns and cities, contributes to the distribution of people within a country.

International migration can be divided into two types: **voluntary** and **forced** (Figure 1.12).

Figure 1.12 Voluntary and forced migration

Voluntary migration is the free movement of migrants looking for an improved quality of life and personal freedom.	**Forced migration** is when the migrant has no personal choice but has to move due to natural disaster or to economic or social pressure.
For example: • Employment – either to find a job, to earn more money or to avoid paying tax • Pioneers developing new areas • Trade and economic expansion • Territorial expansion • Better climate • Social amenities such as hospitals, schools and entertainment • To be with friends and relatives	For example: • Religious and/or political persecution • Wars, creating large numbers of refugees • Forced labour as slaves or prisoners of war • Racial discrimination • Lack of food due to famine • Natural disasters caused by floods, drought, earthquakes, volcanic eruptions or hurricanes • Overpopulation, when the number of people living in an area exceeds the resources available to them

Case Study

Immigrants into California

Back to ...

The New Wider World **pp30–31** for this case study of the migration of Mexicans into California.

Using your case study

Use this case study to answer questions about population migration, within the topic of population dynamics. This is an example of international migration. You will need to:

- explain why people move from Mexico to California
- consider both legal and illegal migration
- describe the types of jobs taken by the migrants
- use Los Angeles as an example.

Update

There are many links within the US census bureau website. One such link takes you to the 'quick facts' section of the website. Go to *The NWW Coursemates* website for a link which gives population statistics on California. It is also possible from this page to link to other sections in the website on California.

Learn it!

1 Explain why people migrate from Mexico to California.

2 Why do you think so many people try to migrate illegally to California?

3 What sort of jobs are taken by the migrants? Why do you think this is?

4 Briefly outline what migrant workers find when they move to Los Angeles looking for work.

EXAM PRACTICE

Figure 1.13 Population change in China

During the mid-twentieth century the Chinese were encouraged by the government to have large families. This resulted in a population growth of 55 million every three years. Concern over this growth rate grew during the 1970s.

In 1979, the state decided to try to control population growth. To do this, family size would have to be reduced to 1.5 children per family. To be on the safe side, it was decided to restrict it to 1.0 – the *one-child policy*. Couples had to apply to be married and again before having a child. Those who only had one child were given free education, priority housing and family benefits. Those who did not were deprived of these benefits and fined heavily.

There were, however, exceptions to the one-child policy.

- Couples could have a second child if the first was mentally or physically handicapped, or died.

- In most rural areas, farmers could have a second child if the first was a girl.
- The 56 ethnic minority groups, who make up 6 per cent of China's total population, were always allowed at least two, and sometimes more, children.

By 1999, the state had begun to relax the policy. The birth rate had fallen from 31 to 19 in twenty years and too few babies were being born to maintain the population. This led to changes in the policy that included:

- all families in rural areas being allowed two children
- giving women, for the first time, an informed choice between different types of contraception
- allowing, in 300 trial districts, the option of voluntary family planning.

a Look at Figure 1.13. This gives information about how China's population changed in the second half of the twentieth century.

   i Why did the population of China grow so quickly during the mid-twentieth century? (1)

   ii How did the government respond to this? (2)

   iii Explain why the government decided to relax the 'one-child policy'. (3)

   iv Give reasons why it is difficult for governments in countries such as China to reduce the rate of population growth. (4)

b Look at Figure 1.14.

   i Describe the population structure of Brazil. (3)

   ii Describe and explain how you think the structure of the population pyramid for Brazil will change by 2050. (5)

c Describe and explain how the structure of population pyramids for MEDCs might differ from that for Brazil, and how they might change by 2050. You may refer to examples that you have studied. (7)

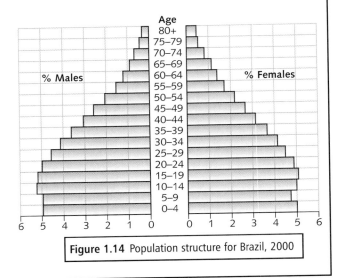

Figure 1.14 Population structure for Brazil, 2000

Back to ...

The NWW Coursemate website to check your answers to the exam practice question.

EXAM TIPS

When an exam question gives you written data, as in question (a), make sure that you use the information rather than just copying it out. Try to use as much detail as possible, but interpret the information. For example, write down what it tells you about population change in China.

In the same way, if an exam question includes a diagram such as the population pyramid of Brazil, you should use information from the graph to reach conclusions. For example, rather than saying how many people were aged under 20, then how many there were over 50, say something like: 'The proportion of the population declined by x%...' or 'There were twice as many people aged over 50 as x...'.

The New Wider World, pp34; 36–38; 42; 44; 46; 50–52; 62; 64–65; 80–81; 83–88

Settlement

2

1 What factors influence the size, development and function of settlements and their spheres of influence?

Settlement types

Settlements are divided into **rural** and **urban**. It is often difficult to tell the difference between the two basic types. This is due to problems in defining the terms *rural* and *urban*, and deciding what makes a village and a town.

Patterns

Geographers are interested in the patterns and shapes of villages and towns as well as in their main functions. Although villages have characteristic shapes, these vary from place to place.

- **Dispersed** This can either be:
  - an **isolated**, individual building, or
  - a group of two or three buildings, perhaps forming a **hamlet**, and separated from the next group by 2–3 km.

  Dispersed settlements occur in areas where natural resources cannot support more than a few people.
- **Nucleated** This is when several buildings are grouped together, initially often for defensive purposes and later for social and economic reasons.

  Nucleated settlements occurred where there was enough farmland for the inhabitants to be self-sufficient, and where the water supply was reliable. They often occur every 5–10 km.
- **Linear** or **street** Linear settlement occurs where buildings are strung out along a line of communication. This may be a main road, a river valley or a canal or dyke.

Site and situation

The location of a settlement is related to its site and situation.

Site describes the point at which the settlement is located. Factors such as local relief, soil, water supply and resources were important in choosing the initial site of a settlement.

Situation describes where the settlement is located in relation to surrounding features such as other settlements, mountains, rivers and communications. The situation of a settlement determines whether it will continue to grow to become a large town or city or whether it remains as a small hamlet or village. Paris, for example, had the *site* advantage of being located on an island in the River Seine which could be defended and which made bridging easier. The continued growth of Paris into Europe's largest city was due to its *situation* in the centre of a major farming area where several routes (rivers) converged.

Early settlements developed within a rural economy which aimed to be self-sufficient. Their sites were determined by mainly physical

KEY QUESTIONS

1 What factors influence the size, development and function of settlements and their spheres of influence?

2 What are the reasons for the characteristics of urban land use zones in LEDCs and MEDCs?

3 What are the causes of problems of urban areas in MEDCs and LEDCs and their possible solutions?

4 How is the environment affected by urbanisation and how can the impact be reduced?

Back to ...

The New Wider World **p36**
Figure 3.6 for a diagram showing the various types of settlement.

Key words to know

Rural
Urban
Dispersed
Isolated
Hamlet
Nucleated
Linear
Site
Situation

Key words to know

Wet-point site
Dry-point site
Nodal point
Bridging point
Aspect

Check this!...

1 What is
   a) a rural settlement
   b) an urban settlement?

2 What are the three main types of village pattern?

3 What is the difference between the site and the situation of a settlement?

4 Explain any three factors that may have influenced the location of early settlements.

factors. An ideal site was likely to have the benefit of several of these factors.

- A **wet-point site**, especially in relatively dry areas, was essential as water is needed virtually every day and is heavy to carry any distance.
- A **dry-point site**, especially in relatively wet areas, was needed to avoid flooding or to be above unhealthy marshland.
- **Building materials**, which ideally included stone, wood and clay, had to be obtained locally as these were heavy and bulky to move.
- **Defence** was sometimes necessary. Good defensive sites may have been within a river meander, with the river giving protection on three sides. A hill with steep sides and good views would be a good defensive site, as for many Mediterranean settlements.
- A **fuel supply** was needed for heating and cooking. In earlier times in Britain, and still today in many developing countries, this fuel is usually wood.
- **Food supplies** were needed from land nearby, some of which was suitable for rearing animals and other areas for growing crops.
- **Nodal points** were where several valleys (natural routes) met to create a route centre or where two rivers joined, as at Khartoum (Blue Nile and White Nile) and St Louis (Mississippi and Missouri), or which controlled routes between hills.
- **Bridging points** may originally have been at a ford in the river, e.g. Oxford in England, or where the river was shallow and narrow enough to allow a bridge to be built.
- **Shelter and aspect** It is an advantage to be sheltered from strong winds, and in the northern hemisphere to have a south-facing aspect as this gives most sunshine, heat and light. In the southern hemisphere a north-facing aspect receives the most sunshine and light.

Functions

The **function** of a settlement relates to its economic and social development and refers to its main activities (Figure 2.1). Usually, larger settlements have more functions than smaller settlements. Large settlements are usually multi-functional (that is, they have several functions), although some functions may be more important than others.

In some cases, the original function may no longer apply. For example, many towns no longer have a defensive function. In other cases, functions have changed over time.

Figure 2.1 Types of function

		Example
Market towns	Originally collecting and distribution centres for surrounding farming area. Today they may service and process agricultural machinery and produce.	Winnipeg, Canada
Mining towns	Developed to exploit local mineral or fuels.	Prudhoe Bay, USA
Industrial – manufacturing	Where raw materials are processed into manufactured goods.	Pittsburgh, USA
Ports	Located on coasts, rivers and lakes for the movement of goods and people from land to sea, or vice versa.	Thunder Bay
Route centres	At the convergence of several natural routes or at nodal points resulting from economic development.	Paris, France
Commercial	Providing the needs of industry and business.	Hong Kong, China
Cultural/ religious	Attracting people, perhaps for a short period, for educational and religious purposes.	Rome, Italy
Administrative	Developed to control areas which may vary from a small region (county town) to a country (capital city).	Brasilia, Brazil
Residential	Where the majority of residents live but do not work.	Marne-la-Vallée, France
Tourist resorts	Include spa towns, coastal and mountain resorts.	Orlando, USA

Hierarchies

The term **hierarchy** refers to the arrangement of settlements within a given area, for example a country or region, in an 'order of importance'. Isolated farms and small hamlets form the base of the hierarchy pyramid. The largest and/or capital city is at the top (Figure 2.2). Three different ways of working out hierarchies are based on:

1 the population size of a settlement
2 the range and number of services provided by a settlement
3 the sphere of influence, or market area, of a settlement.

1 Population size

Early attempts to determine a settlement hierarchy were based on size. However, there is no agreement on the difference between a hamlet and a village or a village and a town. In places like India and China, 'villages' are often as large as many European towns. Figure 2.2 shows the conventional hierarchy applied to MEDCs, in terms of types of settlement.

The divisions based on population size and the distance between settlements, use generalised figures. Notice that the larger the settlement, the fewer there are and the greater the distance between them.

Key word to know

Hierarchy

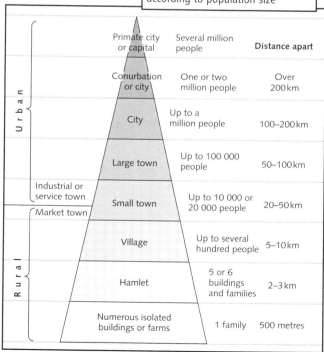

Figure 2.2 Hierarchy of settlements according to population size

		Distance apart
Primate city or capital	Several million people	
Conurbation or city	One or two million people	Over 200 km
City	Up to a million people	100–200 km
Large town	Up to 100 000 people	50–100 km
Small town	Up to 10 000 or 20 000 people	20–50 km
Village	Up to several hundred people	5–10 km
Hamlet	5 or 6 buildings and families	2–3 km
Numerous isolated buildings or farms	1 family	500 metres

Urban / Rural — Industrial or service town / Market town

2 Range and number of services

Villages provide a limited range and number of services. Services that do exist are likely to be used every day and reduce the need to travel to other places. In Figure 2.3, the hierarchy is based on services. Each place in the hierarchy is likely to have all the services of settlements below it.

Figure 2.3 Hierarchy of settlements according to services	
Capital	Cathedrals, government buildings, banking HQ, railway termini, museums and art galleries, large theatre, shopping centre, several universities, international airport
City	Large railway station, large shopping complex, cathedral, opticians and jewellers, large hospital, university, theatre, airport
Large town	Several shopping areas/arcades, railway station, bus station, hotels, banks, small hospital
Small town	Doctor, several churches, cafés and restaurants, railway station, several shops
Village	Church, post office, bar, shop for daily goods
Hamlet	Perhaps none, or public telephone

Back to ...

The New Wider World **p39** Figure 3.15 for diagrams explaining the geographical distribution of spheres of influence.

Key words to know

Sphere of influence
Market area
Threshold population
Range
Central place

3 Sphere of influence

The **sphere of influence**, or **market area**, is the area served by a particular settlement. The area of the sphere of influence depends on the size and services of a town and its surrounding settlements, the transport facilities available and the level of competition from rival settlements.

Note that:
- A **threshold population** is the minimum number of people needed to ensure that demand is great enough for a special service to be offered to the people living in that area.
- **Range** is the maximum distance that people are prepared to travel to obtain a service.

Each settlement that provides a service is known as a **central place**. A central place provides goods and services for its own inhabitants and for people living in the surrounding area. The larger the settlement the more services it will provide and the more people it will serve. Large towns and cities will therefore have larger spheres of influence than smaller villages.

Check this!...

1 What does the 'function' of a settlement refer to?
2 Why do you think the function of a settlement might change over time?
3 What is a 'settlement hierarchy'?
4 Describe the three ways in which settlements may be placed in a hierarchy.
5 Describe the relationship between the threshold population and range for a service.
6 What is a 'central place'?

2 What are the reasons for the characteristics of urban land use zones in LEDCs and MEDCs?

Urbanisation means an increase in the proportion of people living in towns and cities. Although towns were important even in the early civilisations of Mesopotamia and in the valleys of the Nile, Indus and Huang-He (China), most people lived and worked in rural areas. It was not until the rapid growth of industry in the nineteenth century that large-scale urbanisation began in parts of western Europe and north-eastern USA. During the twentieth century, people continued to move to urban areas mainly for:

- more and better-paid jobs
- nearness to places of work and entertainment
- better housing, services (schools and hospitals) and shopping facilities.

Key word to know

Urbanisation

Urban land use models

A model is a theoretical framework which helps to explain reality. Towns do not grow in a haphazard way, but develop with recognisable shapes and patterns. Although each urban area is unique, with its own distinctive pattern, it is likely to share certain generalised characteristics with other settlements. Two of the earliest land use models are shown in Figure 2.4. These models represent the growth of cities in MEDCs.

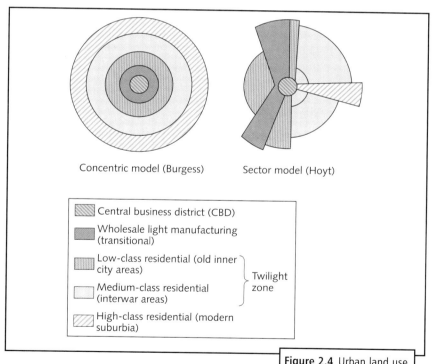

Concentric model (Burgess)   Sector model (Hoyt)

Central business district (CBD)

Wholesale light manufacturing (transitional)

Low-class residential (old inner city areas) ⎫
Medium-class residential (interwar areas) ⎬ Twilight zone
High-class residential (modern suburbia) ⎭

Figure 2.4 Urban land use models for MEDC cities

- **Burgess** claimed that in the centre of all towns and cities there was a **central business district (CBD)**. Using Chicago in America as his example, he suggested that towns grew outwards from this CBD in a concentric pattern. The resultant circles were based on the age of houses and the wealth of their occupants, with building

Key words to know

Central business district (CBD)

becoming newer and the occupants more wealthy with increasing distance from the CBD.

- **Hoyt** proposed his model after the development of public transport. He suggested that urban areas developed in sectors, or wedges, alongside main transport routes into and out of a city. He also claimed that if, for example, industry and low-cost housing developed in one part of a town in the nineteenth century, then newer industry and modern low-cost housing would locate in the same sector.

Urban land use and functional zones

Each of the zones shown in Figure 2.4 has a function.

The four main types of function are shops and offices, industry, housing, and open space. The location of each zone and the distribution of each functional zone are related to several factors.

- **Land values and space** Land values are highest and available sites more limited in the CBD where competition for land is greatest. As land values decrease rapidly towards the urban boundary then both the amount of space and the number of available sites increase.
- **Age** As towns developed outwards, the oldest buildings were near to the city centre and the newest ones on the outskirts.
- **Accessibility** The main routes from the suburbs and surrounding towns meet at the CBD. This has been the easiest place to reach from all parts of the city. Increased congestion now means that the CBD is less accessible.
- **Wealth of the inhabitants** Poorer people tend to live in cheaper housing near to the CBD (with its shops) and the inner city (where most jobs used to be found). These people are less likely to be able to afford the higher transport (private or public) and housing costs of places nearer the city boundary.

Land use in MEDC cities

The central business district (CBD)

The CBD became the most accessible part of a town or city. Because most road and rail routes met there, the CBD could easily be reached by people living in and near the urban area. Its accessibility made it a prime site for several types of land use. Over time, these competed with each other to locate here. This competition, and the limited amount of space that was available, pushed up land values.

The major land users in the CBD became shops, banks and offices. Most located here because they needed to be accessible to the largest number of people possible. Also, only they could afford the high cost of land. Even so, many shops and offices are found in high-rise buildings, where the rates and rents are cheaper. Shops tended to be large department stores and specialist shops which had a high turnover, a high profit margin or a large threshold population.

Check this!...

1 What is 'urbanisation'?

2 Why did people in western Europe and the USA move to urban areas?

3 Describe the main features of Burgess and Hoyt's land use models. How and why are they different?

4 According to these models, what factors affect the location of zones within a city?

Back to ...

The New Wider World **p42** Figure 3.20 for a description of how land values vary across an MEDC city.

Figure 2.5 The CBD

Inner city areas

Many **inner city areas** in MEDCs developed along with industry in the nineteenth and early twentieth centuries. As industry grew, so too did the demand for workers. As more people moved from rural areas to the towns for work, they needed low-cost houses in which to live. At that time, without transport, people also wanted to live as close as possible to their place of work. Despite difficult conditions, people often created a strong community spirit. However, many of the early advantages of living and working in an inner city have become disadvantages.

Houses were generally built as close together as possible, creating a **high density**. The worst type of housing was the **back-to-back housing** in northern England and the **tenement blocks** in Scotland. These were built around a central courtyard in which there might be two or three outdoor toilets and cold-water taps. The dampness of the houses, the lack of sanitation, the closeness of the people and the smoke from the nearby factories made people unhealthy and reduced their life expectancy.

Key words to know

Inner city areas
High-density housing
Back-to-back housing
Tenement blocks

Figure 2.6 Poor-quality inner city housing

Inner cities in MEDCs were often characterised by large factories built during the late nineteenth and early twentieth centuries. They were located:

- on the nearest available land to the town centre and where there was enough space for large buildings
- next to transport routes
- beside rivers which were initially used as a source of power (they also provided water for washing and cooling and were used for disposing waste)
- next to land that could be used to house the large number of workers who were needed.

Since then many factories have been forced to close either due to a lack of space for expansion and modernisation, or due to narrow, congested roads.

Outer city areas

In many MEDCs, cities grew rapidly during the twentieth century, with improved public and private transport. This outward growth, known as **urban sprawl**, led to the growth of large areas of **low-density housing** where residents generally had their own garden, garage, and access to open space.

This was due to the decrease in land values away from the CBD, more land being available towards the edge of the urban area, and the gradual introduction of town planning. These areas rarely had industry nearby and so residents had to travel long distances to their place of work – a process known as **commuting**.

Key words to know

Outer city areas
Urban sprawl
Low-density housing
Commuting

Check this!...

1 What types of land use are found in the central business district (CBD)?

2 Why do you think land prices are so high in the CBD?

3 Why did high-density housing develop in inner city areas in MEDC cities?

4 Why did industry locate in these areas?

5 Explain why housing in the outer areas of MEDC cities is generally low density.

6 Why do many people living in these areas commute to work?

Case Study

New York

Back to ...

The New Wider World **pp50–52** for the case study on New York, an MEDC city.

Using your case study

Use this case study to answer questions relating to cities in MEDCs. You should:

- describe and explain the pattern of land use in the city
- describe problems associated with the growth of urban areas, such as traffic congestion, unemployment and crime
- describe the effects of urbanisation on the environment, for example pollution and the effects of urban climates.

Case study links

Although much of this case study is specific to MEDC cities, it may be appropriate to refer to the location, growth and problems associated with cities in general in your answers. You may be able to link the New York case study to the case study of Rio de Janeiro on page 26, either comparing or contrasting it.

Update

Go to *The NWW Coursemates* website for a link to a site giving detail on the history and development of New York.

Learn it!

1 Describe and explain the pattern of land use on Manhattan Island.

2 List the problems that have resulted from the growth of the city.

3 Explain how any two of these problems are related to the natural environment of the area.

4 Do you think it is fair to say that New York's problems are so bad because the city is so large? Explain your answer.

Land use in LEDC cities

The movement of people to cities in the developing world began in the early twentieth century. Since then it has accelerated so that the population of many places is expanding at a rate of over 25 per cent every decade. The movement from country areas to towns and cities is called **rural–urban migration**. In developing countries, movement to the city is partly due to **rural push** and partly due to **urban pull** (Figure 2.7).

Back to ...

The New Wider World **pp80–81** for more detail on push and pull factors.

Key words to know

Rural–urban migration
Rural push
Urban pull

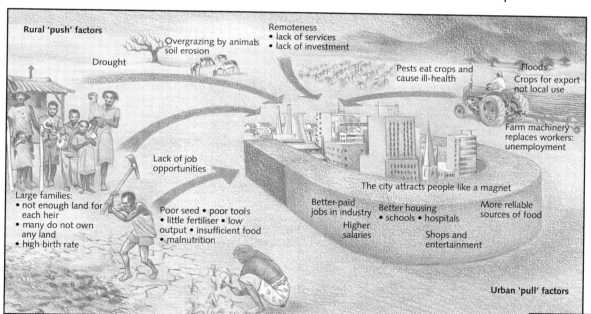

Rural 'push' factors

Remoteness
• lack of services
• lack of investment

Overgrazing by animals
soil erosion

Drought

Pests eat crops and cause ill-health

Floods

Crops for export not local use

Farm machinery replaces workers: unemployment

Lack of job opportunities

The city attracts people like a magnet

Large families:
• not enough land for each heir
• many do not own any land
• high birth rate

Poor seed • poor tools
• little fertiliser • low output • insufficient food
• malnutrition

Better-paid jobs in industry
Higher salaries

Better housing
• schools • hospitals

Shops and entertainment

More reliable sources of food

Urban 'pull' factors

Figure 2.7 Rural 'push' and urban 'pull' factors

Cities in less economically developed countries (LEDCs) develop their own distinctive pattern (Figure 2.8). This differs from the model for cities in more economically developed countries (MEDCs) in several ways:

- Most of the better housing is located near to the city centre.
- The quality of housing decreases rapidly towards the city boundary where many people are forced to live as squatters in **shanty settlements**.

Key words to know

Shanty settlements

• Industry tends to locate along main roads leading into the city centre.

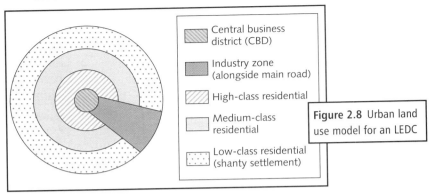

Figure 2.8 Urban land use model for an LEDC

Central business district (CBD)

Industry zone (alongside main road)

High-class residential

Medium-class residential

Low-class residential (shanty settlement)

Case Study

Rio de Janeiro

Back to ...

The New Wider World **pp86–88** for the case study of Rio de Janeiro, an LEDC city.

Using your case study
Use this case study to answer questions related to cities in LEDCs. You should:
• describe the location and growth of the city
• describe the problems caused by the growth of the city
• suggest solutions to overcome these problems.

Case study links
Although much of this case study is specific to LEDC cities, it may be appropriate to refer in your answers to the location, growth and problems associated with cities in general. You may be able to link the Rio de Janeiro case study with the case study of New York on pages 24–25, either by comparing or contrasting it.

Update
Go to *The NWW Coursemates* website for a link giving detailed information on all aspects of Rio de Janeiro.

Learn it!

1 Describe the location of Rio de Janeiro.

2 Outline the main problems caused by the growth of the city.

3 How have the city authorities tried to solve some of these problems?

3 What are the causes of problems of urban areas in MEDCs and LEDCs and their possible solutions?

In MEDCs

The CBD
Over time, CBDs became increasingly congested with pedestrians and traffic. This reduced their accessibility and their attractiveness as places to shop or work.

Many city centres have had to undergo several changes in an attempt to deal with the loss of shops, hotels and offices to out-of-town locations.

The first major change to occur in most city centres was the creation of **pedestrianised zones**. These are either traffic-free or allow only limited access to delivery vehicles and public transport. The advantage

Key words to know

Pedestrianised zones

to shoppers and city centre workers has been a reduction in accidents and traffic pollution and an improvement in safety and in the environment.

Later came the development of **shopping malls**. These are also pedestrianised and are built under cover so that shoppers are protected from the weather and have shorter distances to travel between shops.

Much of the housing built in inner city areas was poor-quality, small, and lacking in many of the amenities present in more modern housing. Over the years, attempts have been made to improve living conditions in these areas. This was initially through large-scale clearance and re-building (**urban re-development**) and later by improving existing properties (**urban renewal**).

In LEDCs

The problems – Kolkata, India

Kolkata is an example of the way in which problems are created when cities grow too quickly.

- **Housing** Many families have no home other than the pavement. Over a quarter of a million people are forced to sleep in the open, covered only by bamboo, sacking, polythene or cardboard. Another 3 million residents live in *bustees*. These are collections of houses built of non-permanent materials, such as wattle, with tiled roofs and mud floors. The houses, packed closely together, are separated by narrow alleys.
- **Water supply, sanitation and health** Although three-quarters of Kolkata's population has access to piped water, it is not uncommon, especially in the bustees, for a single street tap to be used by 35 to 45 families. Sanitation is almost non-existent in the bustees and an estimated one-third of the city's population is without a toilet of any kind. Elsewhere, the old drains and sewage pipes tend to crack, spilling their contents onto the streets. Sewage often contaminates drinking water, especially after heavy rain.
- **Provision of services** The provision of electricity, clean water, schools and hospitals, together with the collection of rubbish, all require considerable amounts of money – which is in short supply to the authorities.
- **Transport** Most people either have to walk or to use the overcrowded public transport system. Many of the buses are old, and there are not enough of them.
- **Employment** Those with jobs tend to work in the informal sector and use their home as a place of work. Often the fronts of houses are 'opened up' to allow the occupants to sell wood, food and clothes. Few people are totally unemployed, but many jobs only occupy a few hours a week, and provide a very low income.

Some solutions – São Paulo, Brazil

Two local government-assisted schemes in São Paulo are aimed at improving the quality of life in a *favela* (slum).

- **Low-cost improvements** Existing homes may be improved by rebuilding the houses with cheap and quick and easy-to-use breeze-blocks. A water tank on the roof collects rainwater and is connected to the water supply and, in turn, to an outside wash basin and an indoor bathroom/toilet. Electricity and mains sewerage are added. Most people who live in this type of housing,

Key words to know

Shopping malls
Urban re-development
Urban renewal

Back to ...

The New Wider World **pp84–85** for further detail on Kolkata, India; and **p26** of this *Coursemate* for the case study on Rio de Janeiro.

Back to ...

The New Wider World **p83**
Figure 5.13 for a diagram
showing a self-help scheme.

which is found in the peripheral parts of São Paulo, have some
type of employment enabling them to pay a low rent.

- **Self-help schemes** Groups of people are encouraged to help build
their own homes. Each group does basic work such as digging
ditches to take the water and sewage pipes. The local authority
then provides breeze-blocks and roofing tiles, and the group
provide the labour. The money which this saves the authorities
can be used to provide amenities such as electricity, a clean water
supply, tarred roads and a community centre. The advantages of
self-help schemes are that they can be done in stages, they can
create a community spirit and, as the cost of building is relatively
cheap, more houses can be provided.

Check this!...

1 Outline some of the changes that have taken place in CBDs and
inner city areas in MEDC cities.

2 Explain some of the problems that face LEDC cities.

3 Describe a solution to any one of the problems you have outlined
above.

4 How is the environment affected by urbanisation and how can the impact be reduced?

Urbanisation affects the environment by causing pollution. Urban
sprawl also affects the environment.

Pollution

Air and water pollution

In Osaka (Japan), for example, the large volume of road traffic, smoke
from some of the older heavy industries and rubbish incinerated at sea,
all cause serious air pollution. Rubbish dumped at sea and oil spilled
from ships, especially oil tankers, pollutes the water of Osaka Bay.

In Rio de Janeiro, an industrial haze, intensified by traffic fumes,
often hangs over much of the city. Along the coast, the beaches and sea
are also polluted. A city the size of Rio produces huge amounts of
waste. In favelas the rubbish is unlikely to be collected and its presence,
together with possible polluted water supplies and the sewage in open
drains, causes health hazards. For example, there was an outbreak of
cholera in 1992.

Acid rain is another form of air pollution.

Back to ...

The New Wider World **p221**
and **pp105–106** of this
Coursemate for information
about acid rain.

Noise and visual pollution

These are also problems caused by the growth of cities, largely due to
the increase in the volume of traffic. In cities such as Rio de Janeiro,
traffic comes to a virtual standstill for several hours each day. In
London, in an attempt to control levels of traffic, drivers have to pay to
take their cars into the central part of the city. In other cities, such as
Paris and Athens, traffic is restricted or banned on certain days when
levels of air pollution are particularly high.

Urban sprawl

The rapid outward growth of cities (urban sprawl) has an impact upon surrounding areas. There is pressure on the **rural–urban fringe** due to competition for land. Figure 2.9 shows a situation that is typical of many cities, particularly in MEDCs.

Figure 2.9 Competition for land at the rural–urban fringe

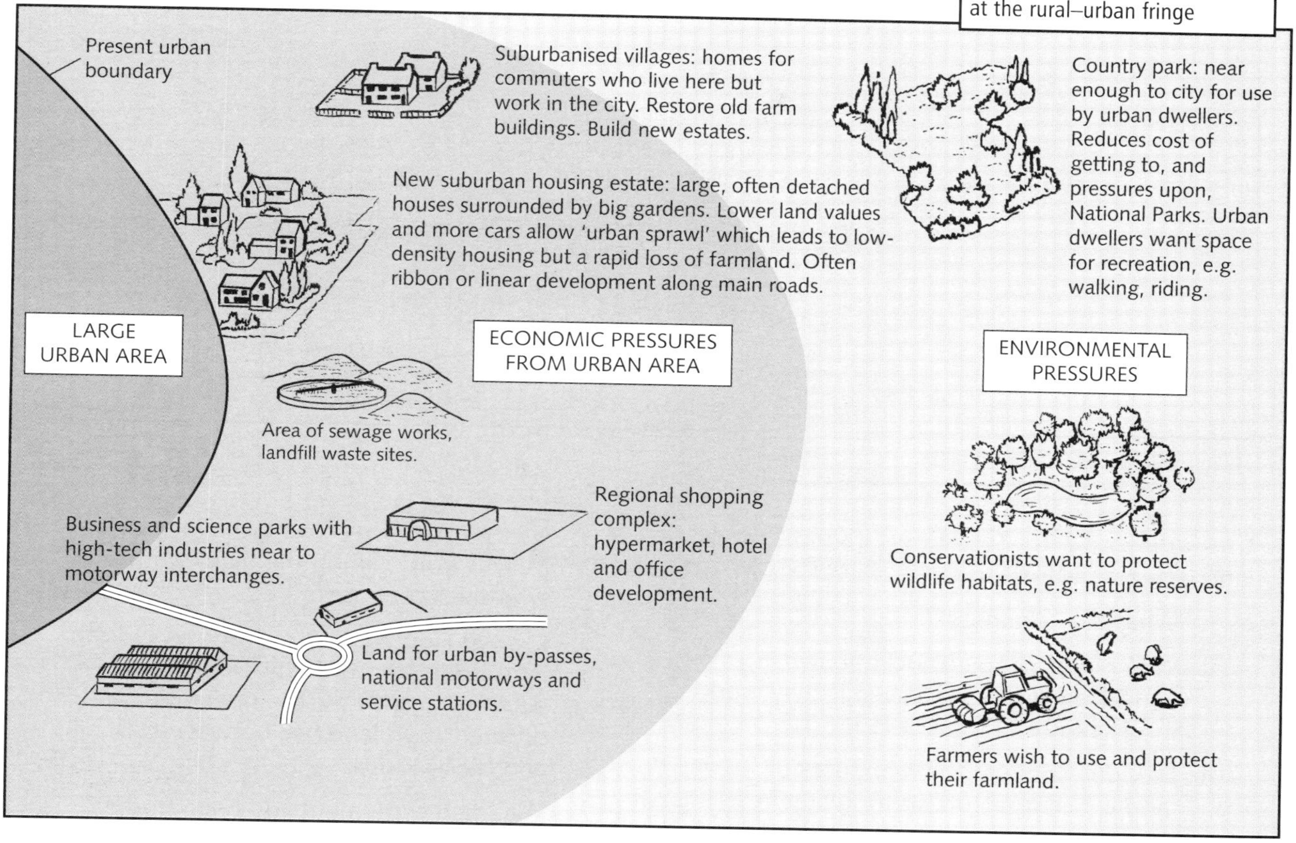

Present urban boundary

Suburbanised villages: homes for commuters who live here but work in the city. Restore old farm buildings. Build new estates.

New suburban housing estate: large, often detached houses surrounded by big gardens. Lower land values and more cars allow 'urban sprawl' which leads to low-density housing but a rapid loss of farmland. Often ribbon or linear development along main roads.

Country park: near enough to city for use by urban dwellers. Reduces cost of getting to, and pressures upon, National Parks. Urban dwellers want space for recreation, e.g. walking, riding.

LARGE URBAN AREA

ECONOMIC PRESSURES FROM URBAN AREA

ENVIRONMENTAL PRESSURES

Area of sewage works, landfill waste sites.

Business and science parks with high-tech industries near to motorway interchanges.

Regional shopping complex: hypermarket, hotel and office development.

Conservationists want to protect wildlife habitats, e.g. nature reserves.

Land for urban by-passes, national motorways and service stations.

Farmers wish to use and protect their farmland.

Pressure on the land at the edge of cities is due to the growth of many out-of-town activities. These include:

- housing development as urban sprawl continues and nearby villages become **suburbanised**
- **science and business parks** with their mainly high-tech firms
- retail parks and regional shopping centres with hypermarkets, superstores, DIY stores and discount warehouses
- office development now that modern technology allows firms a freer (**footloose**) choice of location
- hotels and conference centres which, like science parks, often stand in several hectares of landscaped grounds
- road development schemes, including motorways and urban by-passes
- sewage works and landfill sites for urban waste
- recreational areas such as country parks, playing fields and new sports stadiums.

Attempts to control urban sprawl include:

- imposing planning restrictions on all development (so-called 'green belts') in a particular area
- placing special restrictions on the development of particular land uses, such as out-of-town shopping centres.

Key words to know

Rural–urban fringe
Suburbanised villages
Science parks
Business parks
Footloose industries

Back to ...

The New Wider World **pp64–65** for detail on suburbanised villages; **p141** for science and business parks; **p137** for footloose industries.

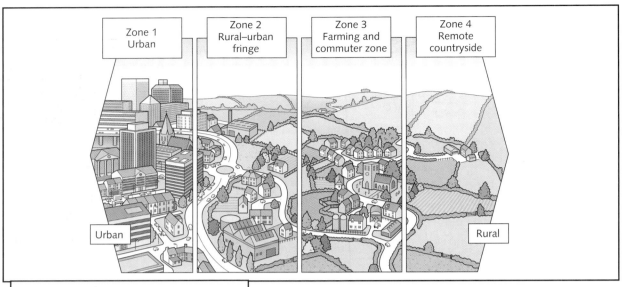

Zone 1
Urban

Zone 2
Rural–urban
fringe

Zone 3
Farming and
commuter zone

Zone 4
Remote
countryside

Urban

Rural

Figure 2.10 Land use in an MEDC

Look at Figure 2.10. This shows a simple model of land use in an MEDC.

a i What is a commuter? (1)

ii Why might people choose to live in zone 3 on Figure 2.10 even if they work in the centre of the city (zone 1)? (2)

iii Describe some of the main uses of land in the rural–urban fringe (zone 2). (3)

iv Why might there be competition for land use in zone 2? (4)

b i Give reasons why towns and cities in MEDCs grew during the nineteenth and twentieth centuries. (3)

ii Look at Figure 2.8, which shows typical land use in an LEDC city. Describe and suggest reasons for the similarities and differences in land use between LEDC and MEDC cities. (5)

c For a named settlement you have studied, describe the problems that have resulted from the growth of this settlement. Outline at least one solution to some of these problems. (7)

Back to …

The NWW Coursemates website to check your answers to the exam practice question.

EXAM TIPS

Remember to check the number of marks awarded when answering an exam question. You could highlight the number of marks shown at the right-hand side of the page. The final part of the question usually carries the most marks, so make sure you spend the most time on this section. The amount that you write should reflect the number of marks given for a question. In particular, do not spend too much time writing a long answer to a part of the question near the beginning that is worth only 1 or 2 marks, even if it is easy. This may leave you with too little time to answer other questions fully.

1 Where are earthquakes, volcanoes and fold mountains found in relation to plate margins?

Earthquakes

Figure 3.1 shows where **earthquake** activity is most frequent. It also locates some recent major earthquakes. The map clearly shows that there is a well-defined distribution pattern, with most earthquakes occurring in long, narrow belts. These belts include those that:

- encircle the whole of the Pacific Ocean
- extend down the entire length of the mid-Atlantic Ocean
- stretch across southern Europe and Asia, linking the Atlantic and Pacific Oceans.

KEY QUESTIONS

1 Where are earthquakes, volcanoes and fold mountains found in relation to plate margins?

2 What are the causes and effects of earthquakes and volcanic eruptions?

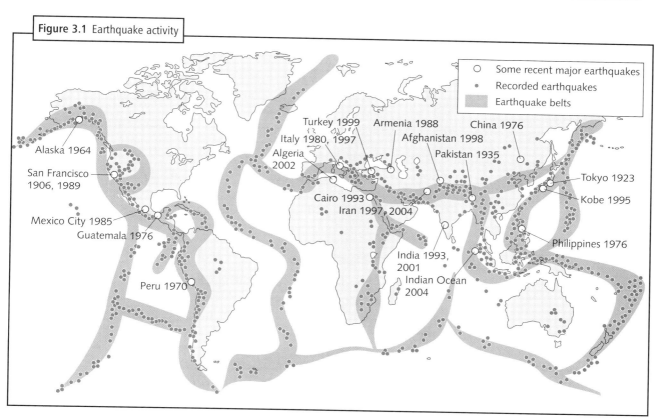

Figure 3.1 Earthquake activity

Key:
- ○ Some recent major earthquakes
- · Recorded earthquakes
- ▨ Earthquake belts

Alaska 1964
San Francisco 1906, 1989
Mexico City 1985
Guatemala 1976
Peru 1970
Turkey 1999
Italy 1980, 1997
Algeria 2002
Cairo 1993
Iran 1997, 2004
Armenia 1988
Afghanistan 1998
Pakistan 1935
China 1976
Tokyo 1923
Kobe 1995
Philippines 1976
India 1993, 2001
Indian Ocean 2004

Volcanoes

The locations of the world's major centres of **volcanic activity**, including some of the most recent major volcanic eruptions, are shown on Figure 3.2. This map shows that **volcanoes** also occur in long, narrow belts. These belts include:

- the 'Pacific Ring of Fire' which encircles the whole of the Pacific Ocean

Key words to know

Earthquake
Volcanic activity
Volcanoes

- the one that extends down the entire length of the mid-Atlantic Ocean
- smaller areas in southern Europe, the Caribbean, east Africa and the mid-Pacific Ocean.

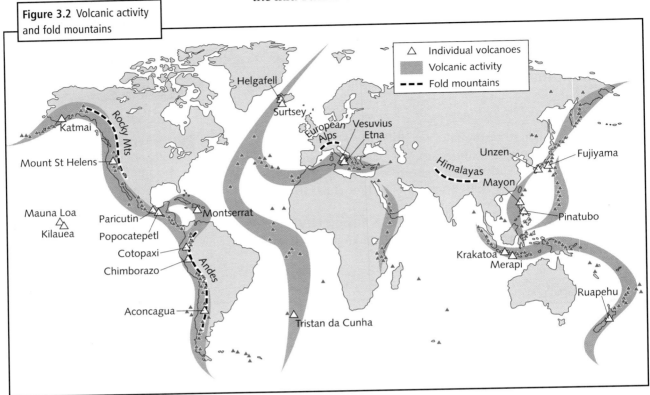

Figure 3.2 Volcanic activity and fold mountains

Back to ...

The New Wider World **p263**
Figure 16.3 for a cross-section through the Earth and its plates.

Key words to know

Fold mountains
Tectonic activity
Plates
Mantle
Convection currents

Fold mountains

The world's major **fold mountains** are also marked on Figure 3.2. Notice how these mountains, although not occurring in long narrow belts, are also located near zones of either earthquakes or volcanic activity.

Tectonic activity

Figures 3.1 and 3.2 show that earthquakes and volcanic activity often occur at similar places on the Earth's crust, and in narrow zones of activity. If the Earth were the size of an apple, its crust would be no thicker than the apple's skin. Underneath the crust is the **mantle**, where temperatures are so high that the rock is semi-molten.

The crust is broken into several large, and other smaller, segments known as **plates** which float on the **mantle** (Figure 3.3). Heat from within the Earth creates **convection currents** which cause the plates to move, perhaps by a few centimetres a year (Figure 3.4). Plates may either move away from, towards, or sideways past, neighbouring plates. Plates meet at plate boundaries and it is here that most of the world's earthquakes and volcanic eruptions occur, and where fold mountain ranges are located (compare Figure 3.3 with Figures 3.1 and 3.2). Very little activity takes place in the rigid centre of plates.

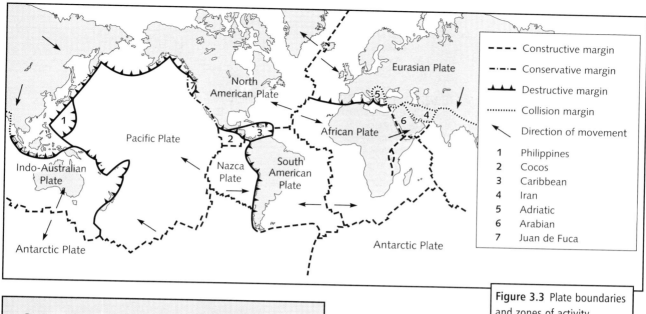

- - - -	Constructive margin
- ∙ - ∙ -	Conservative margin
▲▲▲▲	Destructive margin
∙∙∙∙∙∙∙∙∙	Collision margin
←	Direction of movement
1	Philippines
2	Cocos
3	Caribbean
4	Iran
5	Adriatic
6	Arabian
7	Juan de Fuca

Figure 3.3 Plate boundaries and zones of activity

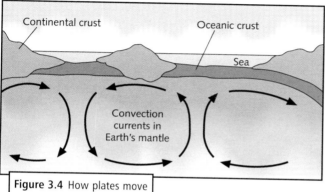

Figure 3.4 How plates move

Check this!...

1 Describe the global distribution of earthquakes, volcanoes and fold mountains.

2 Where do they occur in relation to the Earth's plates?

3 Explain the pattern you have described in question 1.

2 What are the causes and effects of earthquakes and volcanic eruptions?

Plates consist of two types of crust: **continental** and **oceanic**.
- Continental crust is older, lighter, cannot sink and is permanent.
- Oceanic crust is younger, heavier, can sink and is constantly being destroyed and replaced.

These differences in processes, landforms and level of activity at plate boundaries are determined by differences in crust (Figure 3.5).

Key words to know

Continental crust
Oceanic crust
Constructive margins
Magma
Sea-floor spreading
Destructive margins
Island arcs

Figure 3.5 Activity at plate boundaries

Constructive margins

Description of changes

Two plates move away from each other. Molten rock, or **magma**, immediately rises to fill any gap and forms new oceanic crust. This becomes a mid-ocean ridge with volcanoes. The Atlantic Ocean is widening by about 3 cm a year, which means that the Americas are moving away from Eurasia and Africa. This process is called **sea-floor spreading**.

Earthquake/volcanic activity

Gentle volcanic and earthquake activity

Examples

Mid-Atlantic Ridge, e.g. Iceland

Back to ...

The New Wider World **p264** for an account of the creation of Surtsey, a new island off Iceland.

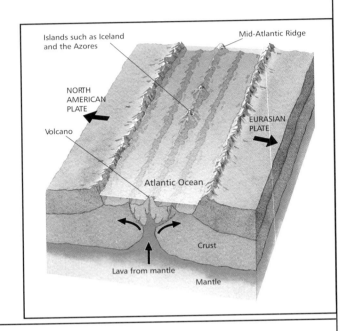

Destructive margins

Description of changes

Oceanic crust moves towards continental crust but because it is heavier it sinks and is destroyed, forming deep-sea trenches and **island arcs** with volcanoes. As the oceanic crust is forced downwards, the increase in pressure can trigger earthquakes.

Earthquake/volcanic activity

Violent volcanic and earthquake activity

Examples

Nazca and South American Plates, Cocos and North American Plates, Juan de Fuca and North American Plates

Back to ...

The New Wider World **pp270–271** for the full case study of the Kobe earthquake in Japan, 1995. This is where the Philippines Plate is forced downwards on contact with the Eurasian Plate at a destructive plate margin.

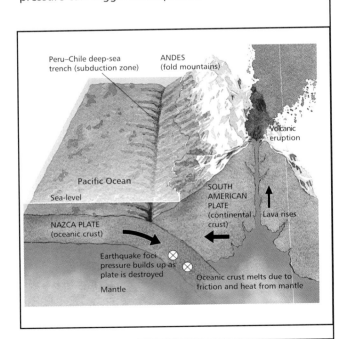

Collision zones

Description of changes
Two continental crusts collide and as neither can sink, are forced up into fold mountains.

Earthquake/volcanic activity
Earthquake activity (no volcanic activity)

Examples
Indo-Australian and Eurasian Plates, e.g. Himalayas. The Indian Plate is moving into the Eurasian Plate at a rate of 5 cm a year. The land between them has been buckled and pushed upwards to form the Himalayas. Evidence suggests that Mount Everest is increasing in height. This movement, which is still taking place, causes major earthquakes, such as the one in central India in 1993 which caused 10 000 deaths and left 150 000 people homeless.

Back to …

The New Wider World **p265**
Figure 16.11 for a map
showing the location of the
1993 Indian earthquake.

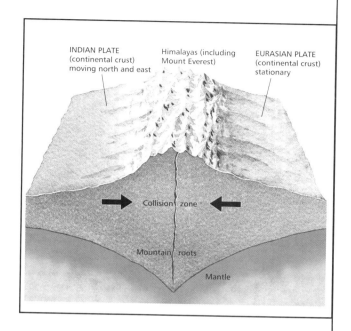

Conservative margins

Description of changes
Two plates move sideways past each other. Crust is neither being formed nor destroyed at this plate boundary, so new landforms are not created and there is no volcanic activity. However, earthquakes can occur if the two plates 'stick'.

Earthquake/volcanic activity
Can be violent earthquake activity (no volcanic activity)

Examples
Pacific and North American Plates, e.g. San Andreas, California. The American Plate moves more slowly than, and at a slight angle into, the Pacific Plate. When sufficient pressure builds up, one plate jerks forward, sending shockwaves to the surface. These shockwaves caused an earthquake in San Francisco in 1906, when the ground moved by 6 m. More than 450 people were killed and 28 000 buildings were destroyed.

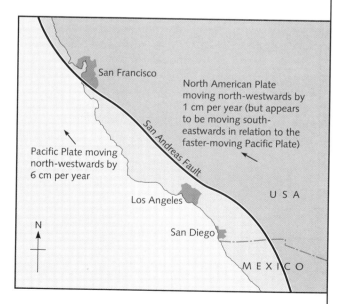

Check this!...

1 What is the difference between oceanic and continental crust?

2 What is a constructive plate margin?

3 Describe landforms that may be found at a constructive plate margin. Give at least one named example.

4 What is a destructive plate margin?

5 Explain why earthquakes and volcanic eruptions may happen at a destructive plate margin.

6 Name two places where there is a destructive plate margin.

Case Study

Mount St Helens, USA – a volcanic eruption in an MEDC

Back to ...

The New Wider World **pp266–267** for the case study of the 1980 eruption of Mount St Helens.

Mount St Helens is an example of a **composite** or **strato** volcano. More than 60 per cent of the world's volcanoes are composite. They are built up through a series of eruptions from a central vent (Figure 3.6). The other common type of volcano is the **shield** volcano.

Figure 3.6 Most common types of volcano

Volcano type	Characteristics	Sketch of volcano
Shield volcano	Liquid lava emitted from a central vent; large	
Composite or strato volcano	More viscous (sticky) lavas with explosive (pyroclastic) debris, emitted from a central vent; large	
Caldera	A very large volcano, which collapsed after an explosive period	

Using your case study

Use this case study to answer questions on plate tectonics as part of Theme 2: The Natural Environment. When answering a question on this topic, you should be able to show an understanding of the main features of volcanoes (and their eruptions) and the effects of volcanic eruptions. This case study presents an example of the effects of a volcanic eruption in an MEDC.

Case study links

Another section within Theme 2 is 'The inter-relationship of physical and human geography' (Chapter 6 in this *Coursemate*). You could use your case study as an example of the hazards caused by volcanic eruptions.

Update

Go to *The NWW Coursemates* website for a link to Volcano World, which provides up-to-date information on the state of the world's volcanoes.

Learn it!

1   Outline the causes of the 1980 eruption of Mount St Helens.

2   Draw a timeline to show the events leading up to and including the eruption.

3   What were the main effects of the eruption:
   a) on the natural environment
   b) on people?

Back to …

The New Wider World **pp268–269** for the case study of the eruption of Merapi volcano in Indonesia, an LEDC.

Case Study

Kobe, Japan – an earthquake in an MEDC

Back to …

The New Wider World **pp270–271** for the case study of the earthquake in Kobe, 1995.

An earthquake is the sudden shaking of the ground that follows a release of energy in the Earth's crust. This is usually caused by movements at the boundaries of the Earth's plates (Figure 3.5). Earthquakes may also be caused by volcanic eruptions.

An earthquake under the ocean floor may trigger a **tsunami**. *Tsunami* is a Japanese word which means 'harbour wave'. This term refers to a series of waves travelling across the ocean with extremely long wavelengths (up to hundreds of kilometres between wave crests in the deep ocean). When these waves approach land, the speed of the waves decreases as they begin to strike the ocean floor (see the case study on the Asian tsunami 2004, pages 38–39). This is when the height of the waves increase. As the waves hit land they may flood low-lying coastal areas, resulting in mass destruction and loss of life.

Key word to know

Tsunami

Using your case study

Use this case study to answer questions on plate tectonics as part of Theme 2: The Natural Environment. You should be able to explain the main causes and effects of earthquakes. This case study provides an example of the effects of an earthquake in an MEDC.

Case study links

Another section within Theme 2 is 'The inter-relationship of physical and human geography' (Chapter 6 in this *Coursemate*). You could also use your case study as an example of the hazards caused by earthquakes.

Update

Go to *The NWW Coursemates* website for a link to the United States Geological Survey, which provides detailed and updated information on earthquakes.

Learn it!

1 Describe the causes of the 1995 earthquake at Kobe.
2 Outline the immediate (or *primary*) effects of the earthquake.
3 What were the longer-term (*secondary*) effects of the earthquake?

Back to ...

The New Wider World **pp272–273** for the case study of the 1998 earthquake in Afghanistan, an LEDC.

Case Study Extra

The Asian tsunami, 2004

On 26 December 2004 the largest earthquake for 40 years occurred between the Australian and Eurasian Plates in the Indian Ocean (Figure 3.7). The earthquake jolted the sea bed vertically by several metres. This displaced hundreds of cubic kilometres of water. At the surface of the ocean, waves travelled outwards from the epicentre of the earthquake at up to 800 km per hour. When the waves eventually reached land, the speed of water decreased but the waves became higher.

Countries as far apart as the Maldives and Thailand were struck by the tsunami. In the days and weeks after the event, the huge scale of the devastation caused by the tsunami became apparent:

- *Indonesia* is the country closest to the earthquake. About 112 000 people are known to have been killed, although many have not been accounted for and the total number of casualties is unknown. The province of Aceh in western Indonesia was devastated, with more than 70 per cent of people living there reported killed. It is estimated that reconstruction will cost $5 billion.
- The southern and eastern coasts of *Sri Lanka* were also devastated. Over 1 million people were made homeless. The infrastructure (roads, communications, etc.) was badly hit. More than 50 per cent of Sri Lanka's hotels were damaged, badly affecting the tourist industry.
- More than 8000 people were killed in eastern *India*, where the cost of reconstruction is estimated at $2 billion.
- The west coast of *Thailand* was also badly hit, and many of the 8000 people killed there were foreign tourists.

The total cost, in terms of people killed and of reconstruction, will probably never be known. By February 2005 it was estimated that more than 300 000 people were killed. The effects of the tsunami were even felt in Africa and other parts of Asia. The reconstruction of the devastated regions will take many years.

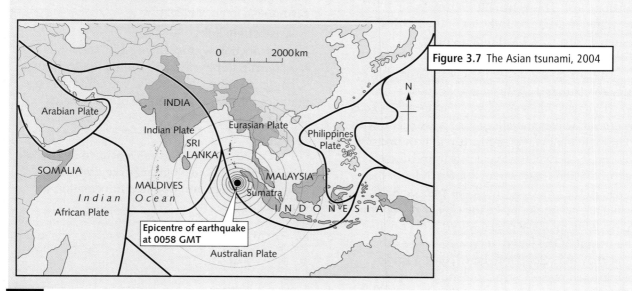

Figure 3.7 The Asian tsunami, 2004

Using your case study

Use this case study to answer questions on plate tectonics as part of Theme 2: The Natural Environment. You should be able to explain the main causes and effects of the earthquake and the tsunami. This case study provides an example of the effects of an earthquake in LEDCs.

Update

Go to *The NWW Coursemates* website for a link giving detailed and up-to-date information on earthquakes.

Learn it!

1 Describe the location of the earthquake on 26 December 2004.

2 Why are earthquakes likely to take place in this region?

3 Explain why the tsunami affected so many countries.

4 Summarise some of the main impacts of the tsunami.

Figure 3.8 sets out the different effects of earthquakes and volcanoes in more economically developed countries (MEDCs) and less economically developed countries (LEDCs).

Figure 3.8 Comparing the effects of earthquakes and volcanic eruptions in MEDCs and LEDCs

Volcanic eruptions

Prediction

It is easier to predict volcanic eruptions than to predict earthquakes. There are several reasons for this:
● Tremors increase within the volcano.
● As magma begins to rise, so do ground temperatures. These can be detected by satellites using heat-seeking cameras (new technology).
● The rising magma causes the volcano to swell and bulge. This can be measured by tiltmeters (which measure slope angles) and satellite global positioning systems.
● Immediately before an eruption, the volcano emits an increasing amount of gas and steam.

Preparation

This includes:
● setting up monitoring and warning systems, using new technology (see Prediction)
● preparing an evacuation plan and organising transport, accommodation and food for those who need to be moved
● training emergency services, such as police, fire and ambulance crews
● organising emergency services, such as water, food and power
● organising post-eruption plans, to include repairing communications and buildings.

MEDCs and LEDCs

The effects of volcanic eruptions are usually much greater in LEDCs, e.g. the poorer countries of Indonesia, Montserrat and the Philippines (Mt Pinatubo). Human

response to volcanic eruptions is usually much quicker and more efficient in MEDCs, e.g. the richer countries of the USA and Japan. LEDCs often have to rely upon, and wait for, international aid.

Earthquakes

Prediction
It is much harder to predict the time and location of earthquakes. However, it is possible to:
● install sensitive instruments that can measure an increase in earth tremors (seismometers), pressure, and any release of radon gas
● map the location and frequency of previous earthquakes to see if there is a location and/or time pattern (this can only give possible timings of an event and not a precise location)
● observe unusual animal behaviour – dogs howling, fish jumping, mice fleeing houses.

Preparation
This includes:
● constructing buildings and roads to withstand earthquakes (Figure 3.9)
● training emergency services and having them available, e.g. helicopters, ambulances and fire engines
● organising emergency services to provide water, food and power
● setting up a warning and information system for use on TV and radio (earthquake preparation is part of the Japanese school curriculum).

MEDCs and LEDCs

The effects of earthquakes are usually much greater in LEDCs, e.g. the poorer countries of Afghanistan and Iran

(1997). Human response to earthquakes is much quicker and more efficient in MEDCs, e.g. the richer countries of Japan and the USA. LEDCs often have to rely upon, and wait for, international aid.

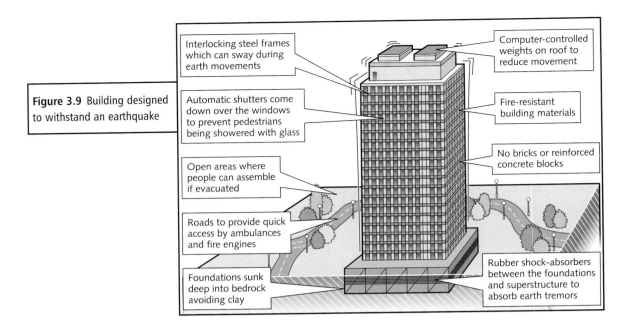

Figure 3.9 Building designed to withstand an earthquake

Interlocking steel frames which can sway during earth movements

Computer-controlled weights on roof to reduce movement

Automatic shutters come down over the windows to prevent pedestrians being showered with glass

Fire-resistant building materials

No bricks or reinforced concrete blocks

Open areas where people can assemble if evacuated

Roads to provide quick access by ambulances and fire engines

Rubber shock-absorbers between the foundations and superstructure to absorb earth tremors

Foundations sunk deep into bedrock avoiding clay

EXAM PRACTICE

a Look back at Figure 3.5.

  i Why do volcanoes occur at constructive plate margins? (1)

  ii Why do earthquakes and volcanoes occur at destructive plate margins? (2)

  iii Why do fold mountains and earthquakes occur at collision plate margins? (3)

  iv Why do you think people continue to live in places where there is a risk of either an earthquake or a volcanic eruption? (4)

b Look at Figure 3.10.

  i Using Figure 3.10 and your own knowledge, describe and explain the areas worst affected by the tsunami. (3)

  ii Explain why the effects of a tsunami may be experienced long after the event. (5)

c With reference to named examples that you have studied, explain why it is difficult for people to prepare for natural hazards such as an earthquake or a tsunami. (7)

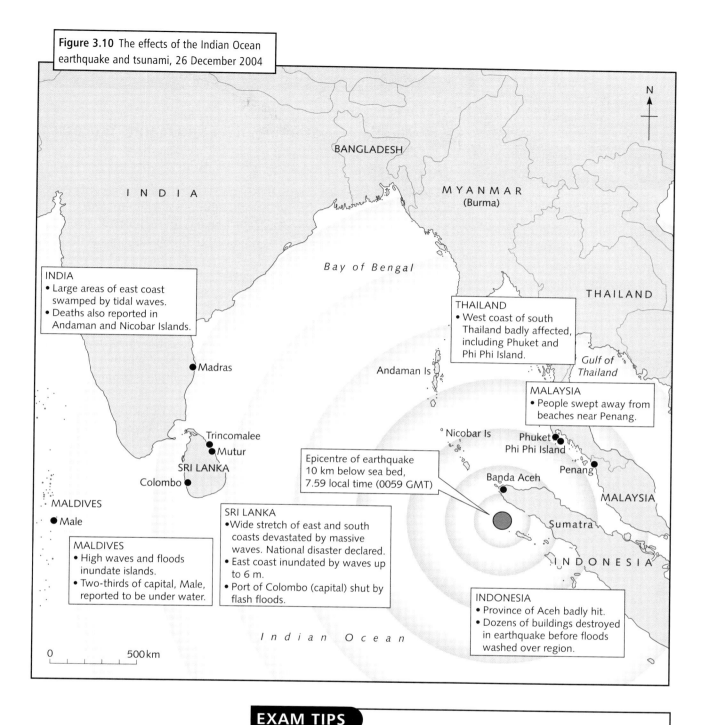

Figure 3.10 The effects of the Indian Ocean earthquake and tsunami, 26 December 2004

N

BANGLADESH

I N D I A

M Y A N M A R
(Burma)

Bay of Bengal

THAILAND

INDIA
• Large areas of east coast swamped by tidal waves.
• Deaths also reported in Andaman and Nicobar Islands.

THAILAND
• West coast of south Thailand badly affected, including Phuket and Phi Phi Island.

Gulf of Thailand

● Madras

Andaman Is

MALAYSIA
• People swept away from beaches near Penang.

● Trincomalee
● Mutur

° Nicobar Is

Phuket ●
Phi Phi Island

Banda Aceh ●

Penang ●

SRI LANKA

Colombo ●

Epicentre of earthquake 10 km below sea bed, 7.59 local time (0059 GMT)

MALAYSIA

MALDIVES

● Male

Sumatra

MALDIVES
• High waves and floods inundate islands.
• Two-thirds of capital, Male, reported to be under water.

SRI LANKA
• Wide stretch of east and south coasts devastated by massive waves. National disaster declared.
• East coast inundated by waves up to 6 m.
• Port of Colombo (capital) shut by flash floods.

I N D O N E S I A

Indian Ocean

INDONESIA
• Province of Aceh badly hit.
• Dozens of buildings destroyed in earthquake before floods washed over region.

0   500 km

Back to ...

The NWW Coursemate website to check your answers to the exam practice question.

EXAM TIPS

Make sure you divide your time carefully when answering the questions in your exam. Each question on Paper 1 is worth 25 marks altogether. You must answer three questions on Paper 1 in 1 hour and 45 minutes. You should spend approximately 15 minutes reading and choosing questions, and checking through answers at the end. This leaves you with 30 minutes for each question. It is important that you spend about the same amount of time on each question, and do not over-run. It may be worth writing the timings on your exam paper, e.g. Question 1: 1.30–2.00, Question 4: 2.00–2.30, etc.

➡ *The New Wider World*, pp230; 245; 246; 248–249; 282–285; 300–303; 318

KEY QUESTIONS

1 What are weathering, river and marine processes?

2 What landforms are associated with these processes?

Key words to know

Weathering
Physical weathering
Freeze–thaw
Exfoliation
Biological weathering
Chemical weathering
Oxidation
Frost shattering
Scree
Onion weathering
Limestone solution

Back to ...

The New Wider World **p246** Figure 15.8 for a photograph of scree.

The New Wider World **p246** Figure 15.9 and **p149** Figure 9.32 (the Sugar Loaf mountain) for photographs of exfoliation.

1 What are weathering, river and marine processes?

Weathering

Rocks that are exposed on the Earth's surface become vulnerable to **weathering**. Weathering is the disintegration (breaking up) and decomposition (decay) of rocks *in situ* – that is, in their place of origin. Unlike erosion, weathering does not need to involve the movement of material.

There are two main types of weathering:

1 **Physical weathering** is the disintegration of rock into smaller pieces by physical processes without any change in the chemical composition of the rock. It is most likely to occur in areas of bare rock where there is no vegetation to protect the rock from extremes of weather. Two examples of physical weathering are **freeze–thaw** and **exfoliation.** Another example is **biological weathering** by tree roots.

2 **Chemical weathering** is the decomposition of rocks caused by a chemical change within the rock. It is more likely to occur in warm, moist climates, because these encourage chemical reactions. These reactions take place most quickly in hot climates, and so this is where chemical weathering proceeds most rapidly. An example of chemical weathering is limestone solution (see below). When oxygen in the air reacts with iron-bearing minerals in the rocks, iron oxides are produced. These are red, brown and orange. This process is called **oxidation**.

Freeze–thaw (also known as **frost shattering)** occurs in cold climates when temperatures are around freezing point and where exposed rock contains many cracks. Water enters the cracks during the warmer day and freezes during the colder night. As the water turns into ice it expands and exerts pressure on the surrounding rock. When temperatures rise, the ice melts and pressure is released. Repeated freezing and thawing widens the cracks and causes pieces of rock to break off. The broken-off rock collects at the foot of a cliff and is called **scree**.

Exfoliation, or **onion weathering**, occurs in very warm climates when exposed, bare rock is repeatedly heated and cooled. The surface layers heat up and expand more rapidly during the day, and cool and contract more rapidly at night, than the inner layers. This sets up stresses within the rock which cause the surface layers to peel off (like the layers of an onion) to leave rounded rocks and hills.

Biological weathering is when tree roots penetrate and widen bedding planes and other weaknesses in the rock until blocks of rock become detached.

Limestone solution is caused by carbonic acid (that is, carbon dioxide in solution) which occurs naturally in rainwater. Although it is only a weak solution, it reacts chemically with rocks such as limestone which contain calcium carbonate. The limestone slowly dissolves and is removed in solution by running water. Solution widens bedding planes and joints to create distinctive landforms.

Back to ...

The New Wider World **p246**
Figure 15.10 for a photograph of biological weathering; **pp248–249** for detail on landforms created by limestone solution.

Check this!...

1 What is weathering?

2 What are the two main types of weathering?

3 Why does the rate of weathering vary in different climates?

4 Give two examples of weathering processes.

River processes

In any river **system**, **energy** is needed for transfers to take place.

About 95 per cent of a river's energy is needed to overcome friction. Most friction occurs at the **wetted perimeter** – that is, where the water comes into contact with the river's banks and bed. The channel of a mountain stream, which is often filled with boulders, creates much friction (Figure 4.1). As a result, water flows less quickly here than in the lowlands where the channel is wider and deeper (Figure 4.2).

Back to ...

The New Wider World **p230**
for detail on energy flows in systems.

Key words to know

System
Energy
Wetted perimeter
Velocity
Discharge
Confluence
Load

Figure 4.1 Water flow in a mountain stream

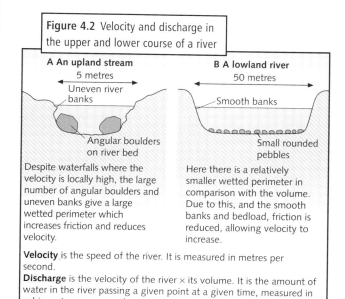

Figure 4.2 Velocity and discharge in the upper and lower course of a river

A An upland stream
5 metres
Uneven river banks
Angular boulders on river bed

B A lowland river
50 metres
Smooth banks
Small rounded pebbles

Despite waterfalls where the velocity is locally high, the large number of angular boulders and uneven banks give a large wetted perimeter which increases friction and reduces velocity.

Here there is a relatively smaller wetted perimeter in comparison with the volume. Due to this, and the smooth banks and bedload, friction is reduced, allowing velocity to increase.

Velocity is the speed of the river. It is measured in metres per second.
Discharge is the velocity of the river × its volume. It is the amount of water in the river passing a given point at a given time, measured in cubic metres per second.

Following a period of heavy rain, or where rivers meet (at a **confluence**), the volume of a river will increase. As less water is in contact with the wetted perimeter, friction is reduced and the river increases its velocity. The surplus energy can now be used to pick up and transport material. The greater the velocity of a river, the greater the amount of material (both in quantity and size) that can be carried. The material that is transported by a river is called its **load**.

Back to ...

The New Wider World **p282**
Figure 17.12 for a diagram
showing the processes of
transportation.

Key words to know

Traction
Saltation
Suspension
Solution
Erosion
Attrition
Hydraulic action
Corrasion
Abrasion
Corrosion
Deposition

Transportation

A river can transport its load by one of four processes: **traction** and **saltation**, along its bed; and **suspension** and **solution**, within the river itself.

Erosion

A river uses the transported material to erode its banks and bed. As the velocity of a river increases, so does the load it can carry and the rate at which it can erode. A river may erode by one of four processes:

- **Attrition** is when boulders and other material, which are being transported along the bed of the river, collide and break up into smaller pieces. This is more likely to occur when rivers are still flowing in highland areas.
- **Hydraulic action** is when the sheer force of the river dislodges particles from the river's banks and bed.
- **Corrasion** occurs when smaller material, carried in suspension, rubs against the banks of the river. This process is more likely in lowland areas where material has been broken up small enough to be carried in suspension. River banks are worn away by a sand-papering action which is known as **abrasion**.
- **Corrosion** is when acids in the river dissolve rocks, such as limestone, which form the banks and bed. This can occur at any point of the river's course.

Deposition

Deposition occurs when a river lacks enough energy to carry its load. Deposition can occur following a dry spell when the discharge and velocity of the river drop, or where the current slows down (on the inside of a meander bend or where the river enters the sea). The heaviest material is deposited first.

Check this!...

1 How is most of a river's energy used?

2 What is meant by the 'wetted perimeter' of a river?

3 What is the 'load' of a river?

4 Outline the different ways in which a river may transport material downstream.

5 What factors will affect the size and quantity of material transported by a river?

6 Describe the different ways in which a river erodes its beds and banks.

7 When does deposition take place?

Marine processes

Most of the processes at work on coastlines are the result of action by waves. Waves are usually created by the transfer of energy from the wind blowing over the surface of the sea. The larger the wave, the more energy it contains. The largest waves are formed when winds are very strong, blow for lengthy periods and cross large expanses of water. The maximum distance of water over which winds can blow is called the **fetch**.

Key word to know

Fetch

Water particles within a wave move in a circular orbit (Figure 4.3). Each particle moves more or less vertically up and down. It is only the shape of the wave and its energy that is transferred horizontally towards the coast. When a wave reaches shallow water, the velocity at its base is slowed due to friction with the sea bed, and the circular orbit is changed to one that is more elliptical (Figure 4.3). The top of the wave, which is unaffected by friction, becomes higher and steeper until it breaks. Only at this point does the remnant of the wave, called the **swash**, actually move forward. The swash transfers energy up the beach, while the **backwash** returns energy down the beach.

Key words to know

Swash
Backwash

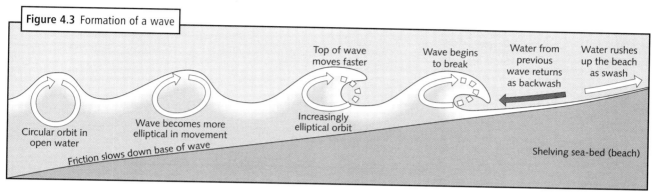

Figure 4.3 Formation of a wave

There are two types of wave (Figure 4.4).
1 **Constructive waves** have limited energy. Most of this is used by the swash to transport material up the beach.
2 **Destructive waves** have much more energy. Most of this is used by the backwash to transport material back down the beach.

Key words to know

Constructive waves
Destructive waves

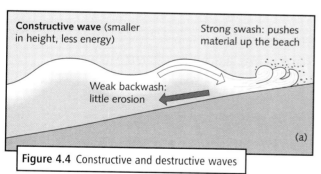

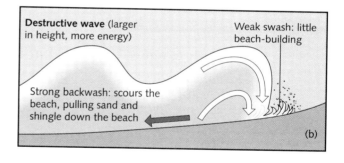

Figure 4.4 Constructive and destructive waves

Erosion
Waves, like rivers, can erode the land by one of four processes:
- **Corrasion** (abrasion) is caused by large waves hurling beach material against a cliff.
- **Attrition** is when waves cause rocks and boulders on the beach to bump into each other and to break up into small particles.
- **Corrosion** (solution) is when salts and other acids in seawater slowly dissolve a cliff.
- **Hydraulic action** is the force of waves compressing air in cracks in a cliff. This can cause pieces of the cliff to break off.

Transportation
Although waves do carry material up and down a beach, the main movement is along the coast by a process called **longshore drift** (Figure 4.5). Waves approach a beach from a direction similar to that from

Back to ...

The New Wider World **p282** and **p44** of this *Coursemate* for detail on how these processes work in rivers.

Key words to know

Longshore drift

which the wind is blowing. When a wave breaks, the swash carries material up the beach at the same angle as the wave approaches the shore. The backwash returns material straight down the beach, at right-angles to the water, under the influence of gravity. Material is slowly moved along the coast in a zig-zag course.

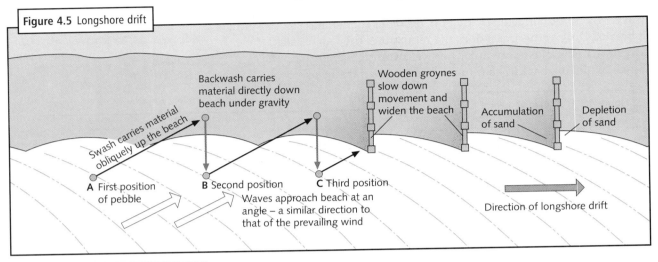

Figure 4.5 Longshore drift

Swash carries material obliquely up the beach

Backwash carries material directly down beach under gravity

Wooden groynes slow down movement and widen the beach

Accumulation of sand

Depletion of sand

A First position of pebble

B Second position

C Third position

Waves approach beach at an angle – a similar direction to that of the prevailing wind

Direction of longshore drift

Check this!...

1 What is the 'fetch' of a wave?

2 Explain the differences between a constructive wave and a destructive wave.

3 What is longshore drift?

Deposition

As sand and shingle is transported along the coast by longshore drift, eventually it reaches an area where the water is sheltered and the waves lack energy, for example a bay. The material may be deposited here to form a beach. Beaches are not permanent features as their shape can be altered by waves every time the tide comes in and goes out. A shingle beach has a steeper gradient than a sandy beach. Prevailing winds may also blow sand up the beach to form sand-dunes.

Key words to know

V-shaped valleys
Vertical erosion
Interlocking spurs
Waterfalls

2 What landforms are associated with these processes?

River landforms in a highland area

V-shaped valleys and interlocking spurs

Any spare energy that a river has near to its source will be used to transport large boulders along its bed. This results in the river cutting rapidly downwards, a process called **vertical erosion**. Vertical erosion leads to the development of steep-sided, narrow valleys shaped like the letter V (Figure 4.6). The valley sides are steep due to soil and loose rock being washed downhill following periods of heavy rainfall. The material is then added to the load of the river. The river itself is forced to wind its way around protruding hillsides. These hillsides are known as **interlocking spurs**.

Waterfalls and rapids

Waterfalls form when there is a sudden interruption in the course of a river. They may result from erosion by ice, changes in sea-level, and earth movements. Many waterfalls form when a river meets a band of

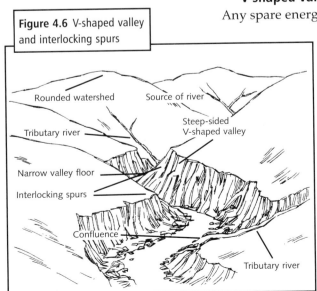

Figure 4.6 V-shaped valley and interlocking spurs

Rounded watershed

Source of river

Steep-sided V-shaped valley

Tributary river

Narrow valley floor

Interlocking spurs

Confluence

Tributary river

softer, less resistant rock after flowing over a relatively hard, resistant rock (Figure 4.7).

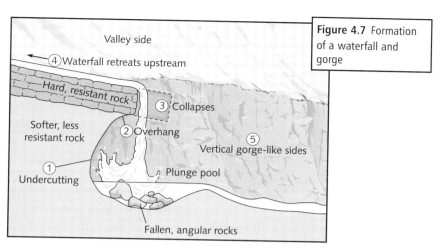

Figure 4.7 Formation of a waterfall and gorge

- Valley side
- ④ Waterfall retreats upstream
- Hard, resistant rock
- ③ Collapses
- Softer, less resistant rock
- ② Overhang
- ⑤ Vertical gorge-like sides
- ① Undercutting
- Plunge pool
- Fallen, angular rocks

Back to ...

The New Wider World **p318** Figure 19.9 for a photograph of a waterfall caused by ice action; **p303** Figure 18.12 for a photograph of a waterfall caused by a change of sea-level.

The underlying softer rock is worn away more quickly, and the harder rock is undercut. Eventually the overlying harder rock becomes unsupported and collapses. After its collapse, some of the rock may be swirled around by the river, especially during times of high discharge, to form **pot holes** and a deep plunge pool. This process is likely to be repeated many times. The waterfall retreats upstream and leaves a steep-sided gorge. **Rapids** occur where the layers of hard and soft rock are very thin, and so no obvious break of slope develops as in a waterfall.

Key words to know

Pot holes
Rapids

Figure 4.8 Angel Falls, Venezuela

River landforms in a lowland area

Meanders and ox-bow lakes

As a river approaches its mouth it usually flows over flatter land and develops increasingly large bends known as **meanders**. Meanders constantly change their shape and position.

Back to ...

The New Wider World **p284** Figure 17.16 for a photograph of river meanders in southern England.

When a river reaches a meander, most water is directed towards the outside of the bend. This reduces friction and increases the velocity of the river at this point. The river therefore has more energy to transport material in suspension.

- This material will erode the outside bank by corrasion.
- The bank will be undercut, collapse and retreat to leave a small **river cliff**.
- The river is now eroding through **lateral erosion**. As there is less water on the inside of the bend, there is also an increase in friction and a decrease in velocity. As the river loses energy it begins to deposit some of its load.
- The deposited material builds up to form a gently sloping **slip-off slope** (Figure 4.9).

Continual erosion on the outside bend results in the neck of the meander getting narrower. Eventually, usually at a time of flood, the river cuts through the neck and shortens its course. The fastest current is now in the centre of the channel and deposition is more likely next to the banks. The original meander will be blocked off to leave a crescent-shaped **ox-bow lake** (Figure 4.10). This lake will slowly dry up, except during periods of heavy rain.

Key words to know

Meanders
River cliff
Lateral erosion
Slip-off slope
Ox-bow lake

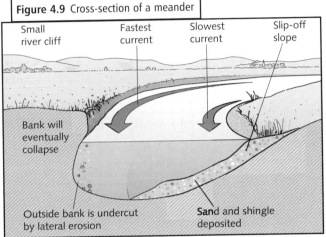

Figure 4.9 Cross-section of a meander

Small river cliff — Fastest current — Slowest current — Slip-off slope

Bank will eventually collapse

Outside bank is undercut by lateral erosion

Sand and shingle deposited

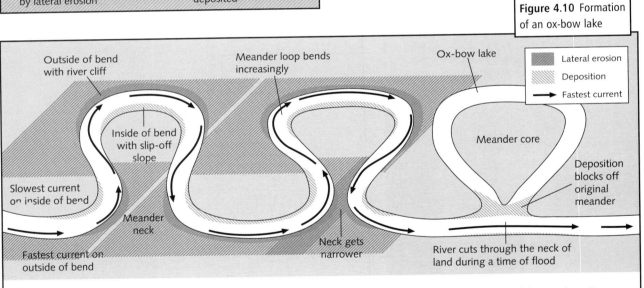

Figure 4.10 Formation of an ox-bow lake

Outside of bend with river cliff

Meander loop bends increasingly

Ox-bow lake

Lateral erosion
Deposition
Fastest current

Inside of bend with slip-off slope

Meander core

Slowest current on inside of bend

Deposition blocks off original meander

Meander neck

Neck gets narrower

Fastest current on outside of bend

River cuts through the neck of land during a time of flood

Continual erosion on the outside of the bend means that the neck gets narrower and narrower until, usually during a flood, the river cuts through the neck and shortens its course. The fastest current now flows in the centre of the channel and there is deposition on the banks. The original meander is cut off, leaving a crescent-shaped ox-bow lake.

Floodplain and levées

The river widens its valley by lateral erosion. At times of high discharge, the river has considerable energy which it uses to transport large amounts of material in suspension. When the river overflows its banks it will spread out across any surrounding flat land. The sudden increase in friction reduces the water's velocity and fine silt is deposited. Each time the river floods another layer of silt is added and so a flat

floodplain is formed (Figure 4.11). The coarsest material is dropped first. This may form a natural embankment, called a **levée**, next to the river. Sometimes levées are artificially strengthened to act as flood banks, to protect the land from flooding.

Deltas

As large rivers approach the sea, they have the energy to carry huge amounts of fine material in suspension. When they reach the sea, the river current may suddenly be reduced, and the material is deposited. Sometimes deposition occurs in the main channel, and blocks it. The river then divides into a series of smaller channels, called **distributaries**, in order to reach the sea. Over time the deposited material of sand and silt may build upwards and outwards to form a **delta**. Deltas are only likely to form where the amount of material brought down by a river is too great for sea currents to remove it (as at the mouths of the Mississippi and Ganges rivers). Some deltas form in seas that are virtually tideless (e.g. the Nile and Rhône deltas in the Mediterranean). Deltas can also form when a river flows into the calm waters of a lake.

Changes in a river from source to mouth

Most rivers show similar changes between upland areas where they probably have their source, and lowland areas where they approach the sea. Figure 4.12 shows the likely changes in the **cross-section** (cross-profile) and **long-section** (long-profile) of a river, in the river's channel and discharge, and in the valley shape.

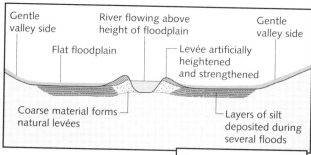

Figure 4.11 Cross-section of a river floodplain

Back to ...

The New Wider World **p285**
Figure 17.20 for a photograph of the Mississippi delta.

Key words to know

Floodplain
Levée
Distributaries
Delta
Cross-section (cross-profile)
Long-section (long-profile)

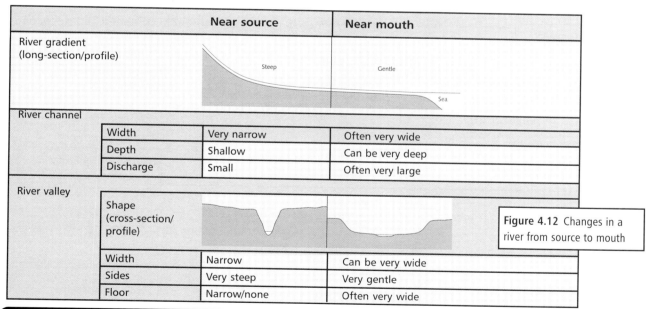

Figure 4.12 Changes in a river from source to mouth

Check this!...

1 What type of erosion leads to the steep V-shaped profile of a river valley in a highland area?

2 Describe how a waterfall forms.

3 What is a meander?

4 How is an ox-bow lake formed?

5 Why do rivers in lowland areas have a floodplain?

6 Describe the conditions under which a delta may form.

Coastal landforms

Headlands and bays

Headlands and **bays** form along coastlines where there are alternating outcrops of resistant (harder) and less resistant (softer) rock. Destructive waves erode the softer rock more rapidly to form bays. The waves cannot wear away the resistant rock as quickly and so headlands are left sticking out into the sea. The headlands are now exposed to the full force of the waves, and are more likely to be eroded. At the same time they protect the adjacent bays from destructive waves.

Cliffs, wave cut-notches and wave-cut platforms

Erosion by waves is greatest when large waves break against the foot of the cliff. With wave energy at its maximum, the waves undercut the foot of the cliff to form a **wave-cut notch** (Figure 4.13). Over time the notch enlarges until the cliff above it is left unsupported and collapses. As this process continues, the cliff retreats and, often, increases in height. The gently sloping expanse of rock which marks the foot of the retreating cliff is called a **wave-cut platform**. Wave-cut platforms are exposed at low tide but covered by the sea at high tide.

Caves, arches and stacks

Cliffs are more likely to form where the coastline consists of resistant rock. Within resistant rocks there are usually places of weakness, such as a joint or a fault (Figure 4.14). Corrasion, corrosion and hydraulic action by the waves will widen any weakness to form a **cave**. If a cave forms at a headland, the cave might be widened and deepened until the sea cuts through to form a **natural arch**. Waves will continue to erode the foot of the arch until its roof becomes too heavy to be supported. When the roof collapses it will leave part of the former cliff isolated as a **stack**. Eventually further wave action will result in the stack collapsing to leave a **stump**.

Back to ...

The New Wider World **p245**
Figure 15.6 for a photograph of headlands and bays.

Key words to know

Headlands
Bays
Wave-cut notch
Wave-cut platform

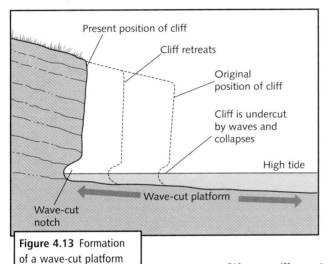

Present position of cliff
Cliff retreats
Original position of cliff
Cliff is undercut by waves and collapses
High tide
Wave-cut platform
Wave-cut notch

Figure 4.13 Formation of a wave-cut platform

Key words to know

Cave
Natural arch
Stack
Stump

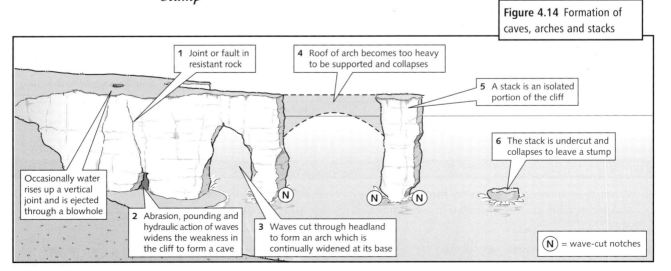

Figure 4.14 Formation of caves, arches and stacks

1 Joint or fault in resistant rock

4 Roof of arch becomes too heavy to be supported and collapses

5 A stack is an isolated portion of the cliff

6 The stack is undercut and collapses to leave a stump

Occasionally water rises up a vertical joint and is ejected through a blowhole

2 Abrasion, pounding and hydraulic action of waves widens the weakness in the cliff to form a cave

3 Waves cut through headland to form an arch which is continually widened at its base

(N) = wave-cut notches

Spits

A **spit** is a landform that results from marine deposition. It is a long, narrow accumulation of sand or shingle, with one end attached to the land, and the other sticking out at a narrow angle either into the sea or across a river estuary. Many spits have a hooked or curved end. They form where longshore drift moves large amounts of sand and shingle along the coast, and where the coastline suddenly changes direction to leave a shallow, sheltered area of water.

In Figure 4.15, line X to Y marks the position of the original coastline. In this example the fetch and prevailing winds are from the south-west. Material is moved eastwards along the coast by longshore drift. After headland X the original coastline changes direction and larger material (shingle) is deposited in water sheltered by the headland (B). Further deposition of finer material (sand) enables the feature to build up slowly to sea-level (C) and to grow longer (D). Occasionally the wind changes direction (e.g. it comes from the east). This causes the waves to alter their direction (e.g. approach from the south-east).

When this happens, some material at the end of the spit may be pushed inland to form a curved end (E and G). When the wind returns to its usual direction the spit continues its growth eastwards (F). Spits become permanent when sand is blown up the beach, by the prevailing wind, to form **sand-dunes**. **Salt marsh** is likely to develop in the sheltered water behind the spit. The spit is unable to grow across the estuary as the river current carries material out to sea. If there is no river, the spit may grow across the bay to form a **bar**.

Coral reefs

Corals are tiny animals that live in colonies and secrete a calcium carbonate skeleton which acts as protection. Over time, millions of these skeletons combine to form **coral reefs**.

Corals feed on algae. Algae are simple plants which use sunlight as their source of energy. Reefs therefore develop in shallow, clear water where light can penetrate. Corals also require tropical or sub-tropical temperatures, and so reefs are found within 30 degrees north and south of the equator.

There are three types of coral reef:
1 **Fringing reefs** – grow in shallow waters close to the coast or are separated from it by a narrow stretch of water.
2 **Barrier reefs** – reefs that are separated from land by a lagoon. These reefs grow parallel to the coast and are large and continuous, e.g. the great Barrier Reef off the east coast of Australia.
3 **Atolls** – develop at or near the surface of the sea when islands that are surrounded by reefs subside. Atolls are surrounded by a lagoon and are usually circular or nearly circular. There are two types: deep-sea atolls that rise from deep sea, and those found on a continental shelf.

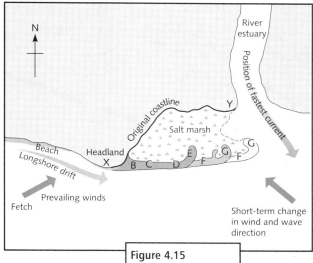

Figure 4.15
Formation of a spit

Key words to know

Spit
Sand-dune
Salt marsh
Bar
Coral reefs
Fringing reefs
Barrier reefs
Atolls

Check this!...

1 Describe how headlands and bays are formed.

2 What is a wave-cut platform?

3 Describe the processes that eventually lead to the formation of a stack.

4 What is a spit?

5 Under what conditions do coral reefs form?

a **i** In which part of a river's course would you expect to see meanders? (1)

ii Describe the typical flow of water around meanders. (2)

iii Explain the processes by which a river delta forms. (3)

b Choose one of the following landscapes:

- river landscape
- coastal landscape.

For your chosen landscape:

i Describe how erosion has formed the landscape. (4)

ii Describe how eroded material is transported. (3)

iii State what type of material is transported, and where and why material is deposited. (5)

c For *either* river *or* coastal landscapes, describe the major landforms and explain how they are formed. (7)

Back to ...

The NWW Coursemates website to check your answers to the exam practice question.

EXAM TIPS

Notice that some questions do not ask you to refer to named examples in order to gain marks. Even so, you should still make use of examples to help you answer the question. It means that you will probably refer briefly to an example, rather than writing about it in detail. In this question, for example, you do not have to give a named example of a river or coastal area in order to gain the marks. But it may help to refer to places that you have studied to explain how the landscapes have formed, or to describe their appearance.

The New Wider World, pp203; 210; 212; 232; 236–237

1 How is meteorological data collected and recorded?

A basic knowledge of weather recording can be obtained by looking at a simple weather station. Although most weather data is now collected electronically, for example using datalogging weather stations, it is still useful for weather information to be collected manually.

Weather instruments

Measuring rainfall

Rainfall is measured using a **rain gauge**. This is located in an open area so that it is not sheltered by trees, and is raised above the ground so that rain does not splash into it (Figure 5.1). Each day the rain collected is transferred to a measuring cylinder, so that total precipitation can be recorded (in millimetres).

Measuring temperature

Maximum and minimum temperatures are recorded daily, using slightly different thermometers. The **maximum thermometer** is filled with mercury. At one point it has a narrow section so that, once the mercury has been forced to rise past it when it expands due to heat, it cannot return (Figure 5.2). This leaves a record of the highest recorded temperature. The **minimum thermometer** is filled with alcohol and contains a metal indicator. When temperature falls, the alcohol contracts, pulling the indicator towards the bulb and leaving a record of the lowest temperature (Figure 5.3).

5 Weather, climate and natural vegetation

KEY QUESTIONS

1 How is meteorological data collected and recorded?

2 What are the main characteristics of the climate and natural vegetation of tropical rainforests and tropical deserts?

3 What is the relationship between the climate and natural vegetation in these areas?

Figure 5.1 Rain gauge

Key words to know

Rain gauge
Maximum thermometer
Minimum thermometer

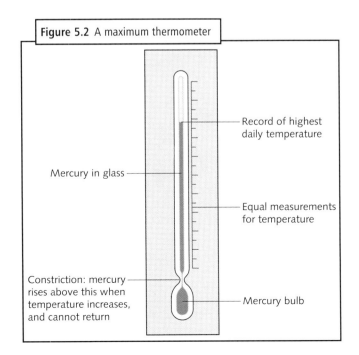
Figure 5.2 A maximum thermometer

Record of highest daily temperature

Mercury in glass

Equal measurements for temperature

Constriction: mercury rises above this when temperature increases, and cannot return

Mercury bulb

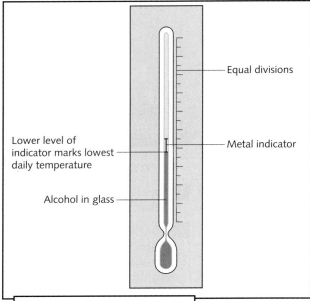

Figure 5.3 A minimum thermometer

Equal divisions

Metal indicator

Lower level of indicator marks lowest daily temperature

Alcohol in glass

Measuring humidity

Humidity is a measure of the amount of water vapour present in the atmosphere. It is recorded using a **hygrometer**, which consists of two thermometers – a **dry bulb thermometer** and a **wet bulb thermometer** (Figure 5.4). As air temperature increases, evaporation from the wet thermometer causes the temperature within it to decrease. The difference between the temperatures measured by the two thermometers can be used to calculate air humidity.

Measuring air pressure

A **barograph** records air pressure in millibars onto graph paper attached to a rotating drum (Figure 5.5).

Measuring wind speed and direction

Wind speed is measured by an **anemometer**. This consists of three cups mounted on a spindle, connected to a rev counter (Figure 5.6). The wind causes the cups to rotate, and the speed is measured in **knots**. Wind direction is shown by a **wind vane**. The arrow points to the direction from which the wind blows.

The Stevenson screen

The **Stevenson screen** is simply a white box on stilts in which are stored the various instruments used to measure air temperature and humidity (Figure 5.7). It has slatted sides which allow a free flow of air. The screen needs to be located where there will be no interference from surroundings that may affect weather readings. For this reason, it is built 1 metre above the ground surface and should be placed away from nearby buildings, on a flat and open surface. It is painted white to reflect the sunlight.

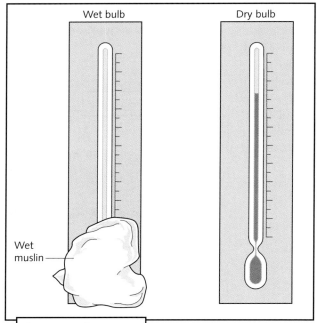

Wet bulb

Dry bulb

Wet muslin

Figure 5.4 A hygrometer

Key words to know

Hygrometer
Dry bulb thermometer
Wet bulb thermometer
Barograph
Anemometer
Knots
Wind vane
Stevenson screen

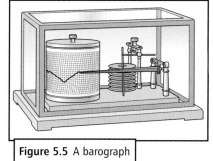

Figure 5.5 A barograph

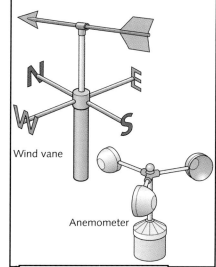

Wind vane

Anemometer

Figure 5.6 Measuring wind speed and direction

Clouds

It is also possible to record the amount of cloud cover.

- High-level clouds form above 6000 metres and are generally composed of ice crystals. They are usually thin and white in appearance. **Cirrus** and **cirrostratus** are high-level clouds
- Medium-level clouds appear between 2000 and 6000 metres, and are often composed of a mixture of water and ice. **Altocumulus** and **altostratus** are medium-level clouds.
- Low-level clouds are usually composed of water droplets, being below 2000 metres. **Nimbostratus** and **stratocumulus** are low-level clouds.
- Some clouds develop to great heights, sometimes as much as 12 000 metres. These dark clouds (**cumulus** and **cumulonimbus**) often lead to heavy rain, and are commonly associated with thunderstorms.

The amount of cloud cover is estimated in terms of how much of the sky, measured in eighths or *oktas*, is covered. The various weather readings may be recorded by means of a diagram showing the weather at a particular location (Figure 5.8). The data gathered may be used to produce a **climate graph**. This shows the average of temperature and rainfall over a longer period of time, usually a year.

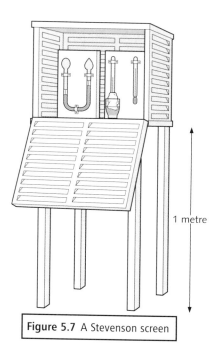

Figure 5.7 A Stevenson screen

1 metre

Key words to know

Cirrus
Cirrostratus
Altocumulus
Altostratus
Nimbostratus
Stratocumulus
Cumulus
Cumulonimbus
Climate graph

Check this!...

1 Why do you think a rain gauge is located in an open area?

2 Describe the differences between a maximum and minimum thermometer.

3 What is a hygrometer?

4 What does an anemometer measure?

5 a) Why is a Stevenson screen painted white?
   b) Why do you think it is built on stilts?

6 How is the amount of cloud cover measured?

7 What does a climate graph show?

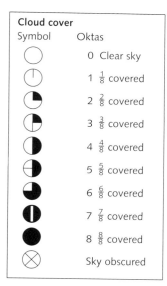

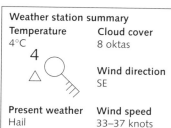

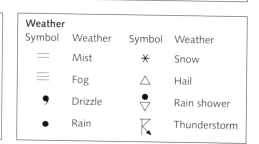

Figure 5.8 Weather recording symbols

2 What are the main characteristics of the climate and natural vegetation of tropical rainforests and tropical deserts?

Tropical rainforest climate

Back to ...

The New Wider World **p212**
Figure 13.3 for a climate
graph of Manaus.

Places with a tropical rainforest climate lie with 5° either side of the Equator. The main areas are the large drainage basins of the Amazon (South America) and Congo (Africa) rivers and the extreme south-east of Asia. Manaus, for example, is located 3° south of the Equator and in the centre of the Amazon basin in Brazil. Temperatures here are both high and constant throughout the year. The small annual range of 2°C is due to the sun always being at a high angle in the sky, even if it is not always directly overhead.

Tropical rainforest areas have annual rainfall totals in excess of 2000 mm. The rainfall is mainly due to convectional thunderstorms which occur during most afternoons throughout the year. These storms are caused by the meeting of warm air masses (the trade winds). The warm air is forced to rise, creating an area of low pressure and giving heavy rain.

Back to ...

The New Wider World **p203**
Figure 12.10 for an
explanation of convectional
thunderstorms.

Some places, like Manaus, may have two or three months with less rain, when the sun is overhead at the opposite tropic (in the case of Manaus this is the Tropic of Cancer). Most rain falls when the sun is closer to being overhead. Winds are generally light and variable. This climate is characterised by its high humidity, a lack of seasonal change, and a daily weather pattern that remains remarkably uniform throughout the year.

The rainforest is a store for vast amounts of water. This water is recycled daily due to evapotranspiration and afternoon convectional storms.

The daily pattern

One day is very much like another, in the tropical rainforest, which experiences 12 hours of daylight and 12 hours of darkness. The sun rises at 0600 hours and its heat soon evaporates the morning mist, the heavy overnight dew, and any moisture remaining from the previous afternoon's storm. Even by 0800 hours temperatures can be as high as 25°C and by noon, when the sun is at a near vertical position, they reach 33°C. The high temperatures cause air to rise in powerful convection currents. The rising air is very moist due to rapid evapotranspiration from swamps, rivers and the rainforest vegetation. It cools at higher altitudes. When it cools to its *dew point* – the temperature at which water vapour condenses back into water droplets – large cumulus clouds develop. By mid-afternoon these have grown into black, towering cumulonimbus clouds which produce torrential downpours, accompanied by thunder and lightning. Such storms soon cease. By sunset, at about 1800 hours, the clouds have already begun to break up. Nights are warm (23°C) and very humid.

Hot desert climate

Places that have less than 10 cm of rainfall per year have a hot desert climate. In most cases, temperatures are high (over 30°C), and so rates of evaporation are greater than precipitation. With low humidity in the atmosphere, a lack of cloud cover and often little vegetation, most sunlight reaches the ground surface. In some desert areas, daytime temperatures may reach as high as 55°C (in the shade). Due to the lack of cloud cover, much of this heat is radiated back into the atmosphere, with the result that at night-time temperatures may drop to near freezing.

As the Earth turns on its axis, it creates gigantic movements of air. Hot air rising over the Equator flows northwards and southwards. These currents cool in the upper regions and descend as high-pressure areas in the two subtropical zones (Figure 5.9). North and south of these subtropical zones are two more areas of ascending air and low pressure. As air rises, it cools and loses its moisture. Still further north and south are the two polar regions of descending air. As the air descends, it warms and picks up moisture, drying out the land.

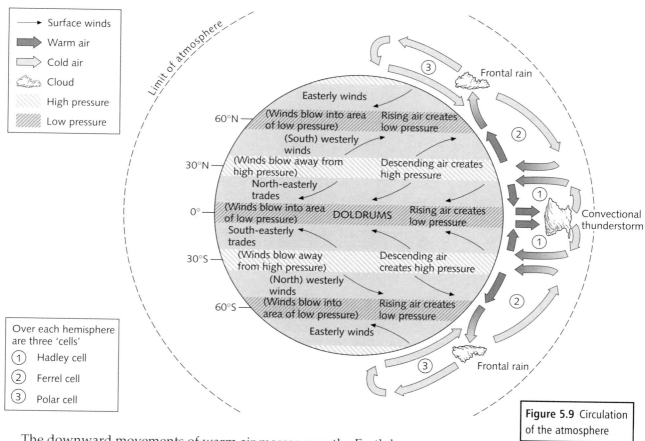

Figure 5.9 Circulation of the atmosphere

The downward movements of warm air masses over the Earth have produced two belts of deserts. One lies along the Tropic of Cancer, in the northern hemisphere, and the other along the Tropic of Capricorn, in the southern hemisphere. Among the northern deserts are the Gobi in China, the deserts of south-western North America, the Sahara in North Africa, and the Arabian and Iranian deserts in the Middle East. Along the southern belt lie Patagonia in Argentina, the Kalahari of southern Africa, and the Great Victoria and Great Sandy deserts of Australia (Figure 5.10).

Other desert areas result from the influence of ocean currents on land masses. As cold waters move from the Arctic and Antarctic regions towards the Equator and come into contact with the edges of continents, they are affected by the cold water rising up from the ocean

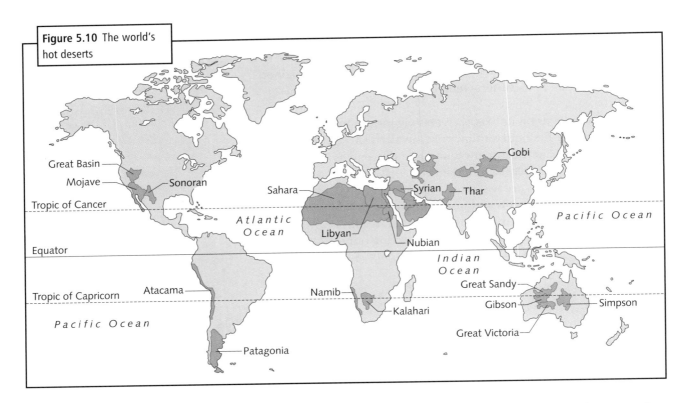

Figure 5.10 The world's hot deserts

depths. Air currents cool as they move across cold water; they carry fog and mist but little rain. Such currents flow across the coastal regions of southern California, Baja California, south-western Africa, and Chile. Although they are often shrouded in mist, these coasts are deserts.

Check this!...

1 Describe the annual temperature and rainfall characteristics of a rainforest climate.

2 Why is there little variation in temperature throughout the day in the rainforest?

3 Describe the climate of a hot desert region.

4 Explain why the world's hot deserts are located near to the tropics.

5 What influences the location of these deserts apart from the global circulation of the atmosphere?

3 What is the relationship between the climate and natural vegetation in these areas?

The tropical rainforest ecosystem

- Tropical rainforests grow in places that have an equatorial climate. The rainforest is the most luxuriant vegetation system in the world. Its plants have had to adapt to the constant high temperatures, the heavy rainfall and the continuous growing season. Over one-third of the world's trees grow here.

- Although the trees are deciduous, the rainforest has an evergreen appearance as the continuous growing season allows trees to shed their leaves at any time.
- Vegetation grows in distinct layers. The lowest layer consists of shrubs. Above this is the undercanopy, the main canopy and the emergents, which can grow to 50 metres in height. Trees have to grow rapidly in order to reach the life-giving sunlight.
- Tree trunks are straight and, in their lower parts, branchless in their efforts to grow tall.
- Large buttress roots stand above the ground to give support to the trees.
- Lianas, which are vine-like plants, use the large trees as a support in their efforts to reach the canopy and sunlight.
- As only about 1 per cent of the sunlight reaches the forest floor, there is little undergrowth. Shrubs and other plants which grow here have had to adapt to the lack of light.
- During the wetter months, large areas of land near to the main rivers are flooded.
- Leaves have drip-tips to shed the heavy rainfall.
- Fallen leaves soon decay in the hot, wet climate.
- There are over 1000 different species of tree, including such hardwoods as mahogany, rosewood and greenheart.
- There is dense undergrowth near rivers and in forest clearings where sunlight is able to penetrate the canopy.

Despite its luxuriant appearance, the rainforest is a fragile environment which depends on the rapid and unbroken recycling of nutrients. Once the forest is cleared, then the nutrient cycle is broken. Humus is not replaced and the underlying soils soon become infertile and eroded. The rainforest is not able to re-establish itself, and the land becomes too poor to be used for farming.

The hot desert ecosystem

Although the climate conditions of the hot deserts are extreme, almost all desert areas support life that is adapted to the harsh conditions.

- Desert plants have developed ways of conserving and efficiently using the water available to them. Some flowering desert plants live for only a few days. Their seeds lie dormant in the soil, sometimes for years, until rain enables them to germinate and quickly bloom. Woody desert plants either have long root systems that reach deep water sources, or have spreading shallow roots that are able to take up surface moisture quickly from heavy dews and occasional rains.
- Desert plants usually have small leaves. This conserves water by reducing the surface area from which water loss can take place. Other plants drop their leaves during the dry period. In desert plants the process of photosynthesis takes place in the stems rather than (as in other plants) in leaves. Many desert plants store water in leaves, stems and roots. Thorns, which are modified leaves, serve to guard the water from animal invaders. These plants may take in and store carbon dioxide only at night; during the day their stomata, or pores, are closed to prevent evaporation.

Back to …

The New Wider World **p232** Figure 14.8 for a diagram showing the vegetation layers in the tropical rainforest.

The New Wider World **p232** Figure 14.9 for a photograph of a tree in the rainforest with buttress roots.

Back to …

The New Wider World **p232** Figure 14.10 for a diagram showing nutrient cycling in the rainforest; **pp236–237** for the effects of forest clearance.

Check this!...

1 Describe how vegetation in the rainforest has adapted to the climate.

2 Why may the rainforest be described as a 'fragile ecosystem'?

3 How has vegetation adapted to the climate of desert areas?

a i What is a hygrometer? (1)

ii A hygrometer is usually kept in a Stevenson screen. What is the purpose of a Stevenson screen? (2)

iii Describe how the speed and direction of wind are measured and recorded. (3)

iv How is the amount of cloud cover measured and recorded? (4)

b Look at Figure 5.11.

i Describe the location of Walvis Bay. (3)

ii Draw a climate graph to show the information in Figure 5.11. (5)

iii Describe and explain the information shown in your graph. (7)

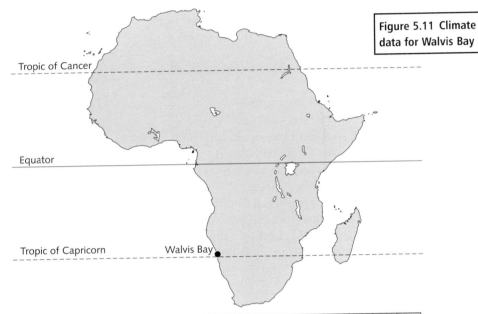

Figure 5.11 Climate data for Walvis Bay

Tropic of Cancer

Equator

Tropic of Capricorn   Walvis Bay

Walvis Bay (7 metres)	Jan	Feb	Mar	Apr	May	Jun	Jul	Aug	Sep	Oct	Nov	Dec
Temperature – max.(°C)	23	23	23	24	23	23	21	20	19	19	22	22
Temperature – min.(°C)	15	16	15	13	11	9	8	8	9	11	12	14
Rainfall(mm)	0	5	8	3	3	0	0	3	0	0	0	0

Back to ...

The NWW Coursemates website to check your answers to the exam practice question.

The inter-relationships between the natural environment and human activities

How does the natural environment present hazards and offer opportunities for human activities?

Natural processes have impacts on people, which may be positive or negative. A volcanic eruption, for example, is a natural process. When it affects people it becomes a **hazard.** These hazards not only cause problems for people, they may also bring benefits. A volcanic region can provide rich fertile soils as well as experience the dangers brought by eruptions. Some of the most common hazards are shown in Figure 6.1.

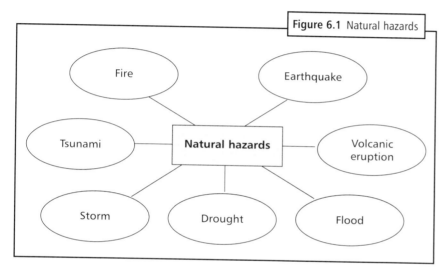

Figure 6.1 Natural hazards

KEY QUESTION

How does the natural environment present hazards and offer opportunities for human activities?

Back to …

Chapter 3 pp 31–41 of this *Coursemate* for information on earthquakes and volcanic eruptions.

Tropical storms

Tropical storms are areas of intensive low pressure known locally as **hurricanes**, **typhoons** or **cyclones** (Figure 6.2).

Key words to know

Hazard
Tropical storms
Hurricanes
Typhoons
Cyclones

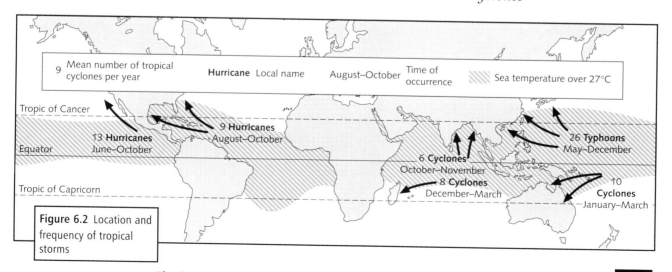

9 Mean number of tropical cyclones per year   **Hurricane** Local name   August–October Time of occurrence   Sea temperature over 27°C

Tropic of Cancer

13 **Hurricanes** June–October

9 **Hurricanes** August–October

Equator

6 **Cyclones** October–November

8 **Cyclones** December–March

26 **Typhoons** May–December

Tropic of Capricorn

10 **Cyclones** January–March

Figure 6.2 Location and frequency of tropical storms

Tropical storms tend to develop:

- over warm tropical oceans, where sea temperatures are greater than 27°C over a very large area, and where there is a considerable depth of warm water
- in late summer and early autumn, when sea temperatures are at their highest
- in the trade wind belt, between latitudes 5° and 20° north and south of the Equator.

The formation of tropical storms is not completely understood. However, they appear to originate when a strong vertical movement of air draws with it water vapour from the ocean below. As the air rises, in a spiral movement, it cools and condenses. This process releases enormous amounts of heat energy.

Effects

Tropical storms are a major hazard that can cause considerable loss of life and damage to property and to a country's economy.

- **Winds** often exceed 160 km/hr (and can reach 250 km/hr). Many LEDCs lie in the tropical cyclone belt, and whole villages in these countries may be destroyed. Even in more economically developed countries (MEDCs), where people have money to reinforce buildings, houses and coastal developments can be severely damaged. High winds uproot trees and disrupt telephone and electricity power supplies. Worst-hit are those less economically developed countries (LEDCs) that have their only export crop destroyed.
- **Flooding**, caused by the torrential rain, is often the major cause of death. It can also pollute water supplies, increasing the risk of cholera.
- **Storm (tidal) surges**, up to 5 metres and heightened by storm waves, flood low-lying coastal areas causing loss of life and blocking escape and relief roads.
- **Landslides** occur where heavy rainfall washes away buildings erected on steep, unstable slopes.

Back to …

The New Wider World **p312** for information on how tropical storms cause coastal flooding.

The Gulf of Mexico

Tropical storms are a major annual hazard to countries surrounding the Gulf of Mexico. However, their short-term and long-term effects are usually much greater in the LEDCs of Central America and the Caribbean than in the MEDC of the USA. Two of the worst storms to hit each area in recent years are described in Figure 6.3.

Figure 6.3 Hurricane Mitch
and Hurricane Andrew

	LEDC – Hurricane Mitch	MEDC – Hurricane Andrew
Location	Nicaragua, Honduras, Guatemala, El Salvador	USA – Florida
Deaths	Over 12 000	30
Missing	Over 16 000	15
Homeless	700 000	80 000
Number affected	3 million	1.3 million
Time for help to arrive	Several days	Within hours
Effect on services	No telephones, electricity, fresh water or transport	No telephones or electricity
Effect on economy	Crops lost/damaged – often the only product for sale/export: long-term	Many businesses forced to close until electricity restored: short-term
Secondary effects	Shortages of food, clothing, medical supplies. Fear of cholera	Very few
Prediction	Less effective early warning system. Some people without TV/radio to hear warning	Effective early warning system. People able to hear warnings on TV/radio
Planning	Limited emergency services and equipment. Few available hospitals and doctors. Many houses flimsy and poorly built – easily blown down/washed away. Not insured	Emergency services well trained and equipped. Houses strongly built and reinforced. Many hospitals, doctors and ambulances. Houses insured
Time to recover	Estimated 10 years	Within a few days

Check this!...

1 What is a 'natural hazard'?

2 Describe the global distribution of tropical storms.

3 What are the main effects of tropical storms?

4 Explain why the effects of tropical storms vary between MEDCs and LEDCs.

Flooding

Extreme weather conditions are the most common cause of a river flooding. The amount of water in a river may be increased by:
- a torrential thunderstorm
- continuous rainfall for several days, or
- rain following a heavy snowfall so that it melts rapidly.

At other times, high summer temperatures increase evapotranspiration and so may reduce the amount of water reaching a river. High temperatures can also make the ground hard, so that less water can sink into (infiltrate) the ground when it does rain. In winter, if the ground is frozen, water cannot penetrate the ground, which is described as being 'impermeable'. In both these cases, the water flows over the ground surface and so fills a river more rapidly.

The effects of a major river flood may be as severe in an MEDC (e.g. the Mississippi in the USA in 1993, the Elbe in Germany in 2002) as in an LEDC. However, in an LEDC money and technology are limited, so relief operations are more likely to be slower and less effective. It also takes an LEDC much longer to recover from flooding.

Flooding in Bangladesh, 1998

Causes

- Much of Bangladesh consists of the floodplain of the Ganges and Brahmaputra rivers. Over half the country lies less than 6 metres above sea-level. Once the rivers overflow their banks or breach the protective floodbanks (levées), the water can spread over huge distances, flooding roads, railways, farmland and settlements.
- Bangladesh has a monsoon climate, with most places receiving between 1800 and 2600 mm of rain a year. However, 80 per cent of that total is concentrated in just four or five months (June to September).
- The period of heavy rain coincides with the highest temperatures. These temperatures melt ice and snow in the Himalayas where the Ganges, Brahmaputra and their tributaries originate, adding to the water in the rivers.
- Global warming is causing glaciers in the Himalayas to melt (increasing runoff) and sea-level in the Bay of Bengal to rise.
- The monthly high spring tides and the effect of tropical storms, which are most frequent in summer and autumn, can prevent floodwater escaping into the sea.
- Silt is brought down by the rivers and deposited within their channels. This raises the height of the river beds and so increases the risk of flooding.
- Human mismanagement has increased the magnitude and frequency of flooding by:
  - building on the floodplains to house the country's growing population (this is the process of urbanisation
  - cutting down trees in the upper drainage basin (e.g. Nepal) – deforestation increases the rate and amount of runoff.

Effects

At its peak, the 1998 flood was so deep that in some places only the tops of trees and buildings could be seen. Railways, roads and bridges were swept away. Most parts of the country were without electricity for several weeks and, because floodwater polluted wells, there was no safe drinking water. Hospitals were full of people suffering from dysentery and diarrhoea. The threat of disease, especially cholera, increased. Parts of Dhaka, the capital of Bangladesh, including the international airport, were under 2 metres of water. It became very difficult to deliver overseas aid, including food and medical supplies.

It is important to note that flooding is an annual event in Bangladesh, which brings both benefits and problems to the country. The monsoon rains cause rivers such as the Jamuna (Brahmaputra) and Padma (Ganges) to overflow their banks between July and mid-August, flooding about 20 per cent of the country. Most of Bangladesh's 140 million people live on the floodplains of these rivers. For most of them, the seasonal flood is essential for their survival as it brings water in which to grow the main crops of rice and jute. It also leaves behind silt which fertilises the fields. Flooding is considered beneficial for crops and the ecological balance.

Back to ...

The New Wider World **p288** for background information on the flooding in Bangladesh in 1998.

Back to ...

The New Wider World **p124** for information about the monsoon climate.

Back to ...

The New Wider World **p219** and **pp101–104** of this *Coursemate* for information about global warming.

Back to ...

The New Wider World **pp216–217** and **pp61–63** of this *Coursemate* for information about tropical storms.

Check this!...

1 What is the most common cause of river flooding?

2 Why may the effects of flooding in an LEDC be greater than in an MEDC?

3 Describe the main causes of the floods in Bangladesh in 1998.

4 a) Which effects of the flooding do you think were short-term?

   b) Which do you think affected the country for a longer period of time?

Inter-relationships between the natural environment and human activities in rainforests and deserts

Desertification

The word **desertification** means 'turning the land into desert'. It is mainly a problem in hot desert areas, but it is becoming a more widespread global issue.

Key word to know

Desertification

Case Study

Desertification in the Sahel

Back to ...

The New Wider World **pp256–258** for the case study of desertification in the Sahel.

Update

Go to *The NWW Coursemates* website for a link to Friends of Eden, which gives a comprehensive picture of the Sahel.

Using your case study

Use this case study to answer questions about the impact of people on hot desert climate regions. You should know:

- what desertification is
- the main features of the Sahel region
- the main causes of desertification
  - climate change
  - overgrazing
  - population growth
- the results of desertification.

Case study links

The issue of desertification is linked to the provision of water supplies. Therefore it may be appropriate to use this case study in the section on energy and water resources.

Learn it!

1 What is desertification?

2 Which regions of the world are most at risk from desertification?

3 What are the main features of the Sahel region of Africa?

4 Why is this region affected by desertification?

5 What are the results of desertification in the Sahel?

Deforestation: why is Brazil's rainforest being cleared?

One-third of the world's trees grow in the Brazilian rainforest. However, their numbers are falling rapidly due to **deforestation**.

Brazil's population has grown rapidly since the 1960s. This means that to improve people's standard of living:

- more land was needed for people to live on
- more farmland was needed to produce food for the extra numbers
- more jobs were required for people to earn a living
- more resources were needed.

The country also needed to reduce its huge national debt. At that time the Brazilian rainforest was largely undeveloped, and it had plenty of space and many resources.

Back to ...

The New Wider World **p232** Figure 14.10 for some of the effects of deforestation.

Key word to know

Deforestation

Farming

Land in the rainforest is cleared for three types of farming.

1 **'Slash and burn'** is the traditional method used by the Amerindians of the rainforest. Although this is the most sustainable of the three types, it still means that considerable areas are cleared, even if only temporarily, each year.

2 **Subsistence farming** has increased because the government provides land to some of Brazil's 25 million landless people. In places, 10 km strips of land were cleared alongside highways, and settlers were brought in from places that were even poorer, like the drought areas in the north-east.

3 **Commercial cattle ranching** is run by large transnational companies which sell beef mainly to fast-food chains in developed countries. These companies burn the forest, replacing trees with grass (Figure 6.4).

Key words to know

Slash and burn farming
Subsistence farming
Commercial cattle ranching

Figure 6.4 Commercial cattle ranching in the former rainforest

Transport

Over 12 000 km of new roads have been built across the rainforest. The largest of these is the 5300 km Trans-Amazonian highway. Roads were built to develop the region and to transport timber, minerals, farm produce and people. A 900 km railway has been built from Carajas to the coast. Many small airstrips have also been constructed.

Resources

The main types of resource in the rainforest are:

1 **Timber**, mainly hardwood, is obtained by logging companies which fell trees to sell in MEDCs. Timber is a valuable source of income for Brazil, but little attempt has been made to replant deforested areas.

2 **Minerals** provide the region with a vast natural resource. They include iron ore, bauxite, manganese, diamonds, gold and silver.

3 **Hydro-electricity** is an important renewable source of energy but the building of dams and the creation of large lakes has led to large areas of forest being flooded.

Back to ...

The New Wider World
pp236–237 Figures 14.19, 14.21 and 14.23 for photographs showing the results of deforestation; p237 for information on the rates of deforestation.

Settlement

The development of Amazonia has led to an increase in population from 2 million (1960) to over 30 million (2000). Large tracts of forest have been cleared for the development of such new settlements as Maraba (150 000) and Carajas.

What are the effects of the clearance?

- Of 30 million known animal and plant species on the Earth, 28 million are found in the rainforest (99 per cent of these are insects). Many others have still to be identified and studied. Deforestation has destroyed the habitats of many of these species – some may have had considerable value. (We already get more than half of our medicines from the rainforest.)

- There has been a huge reduction in the number of Amerindian people (from 6 million when Europeans arrived to the present number of 200 000), and much of their traditional culture and way of life has been destroyed. Those who remain are often forced to live on reservations.

- The clearance of trees means that there is no canopy to protect the soil from the heavy afternoon rain, and no roots to hold the soil together. As a result, less water is intercepted by leaves, less water penetrates the soil, and more flows over the surface as runoff. This means the soil is eroded by the water. Deforestation also breaks the humus cycle and any nutrients are rapidly washed (leached) out of the soil, leaving it infertile. Some of the new subsistence farms and the larger cattle ranches have had to be abandoned because of this loss in fertility.

- Many rivers have been polluted by mining operations.

- Deforestation is causing climatic change in two ways. Because there are fewer trees there is less evapotranspiration and, therefore, less water vapour in the air. (About one-quarter of the world's fresh water is, at present, stored in the Amazon basin.) With less moisture in the hydrological cycle, there is already evidence of reduced rainfall totals, and the threat of more local droughts. At the same time, the burning of the forest is accelerating global warming by releasing huge amounts of carbon dioxide, which is the main greenhouse gas.

- It is possible that there are already changes in the composition of the atmosphere. Scientists claim that over one-third of the world's fresh oxygen supply comes from the tropical rainforest. This would be lost if the region is totally deforested.

Back to …

The New Wider World **p254** and **pp106–108** of this *Coursemate* for information about soil erosion.

Back to …

The New Wider World **p239** for information about deforestation of the rainforest in Malaysia; **p240** for how forestry may be managed to protect the environment.

Check this!…

1 What is deforestation?

2 Give two reasons to explain why deforestation is taking place in the Brazilian rainforest.

3 Do you think the effects of deforestation in the Amazon are a problem just for Brazil, or is deforestation a global issue?

EXAM PRACTICE

a Look at Figure 6.2, which shows information about tropical storms.

   i   What is a tropical storm? (1)

   ii Why are such storms usually found only in tropical regions? (2)

   iii Describe the location and movement of the storms shown on Figure 6.2. (3)

   iv Although the exact path of a tropical storm is hard to predict, there is usually some warning before a storm arrives. Explain what people could do during a storm to protect themselves. (4)

b i   Long-term effects may occur in the weeks or months after a large volcanic eruption. Explain why these long-term effects may be difficult to deal with. (3)

   ii How might these effects differ between MEDCs and LEDCs? (5)

c With reference to at least one volcanic eruption you have studied, describe the short-term and long-term effects of the eruption. (7)

Back to ...

The NWW Coursemates website to check your answers to the exam practice question.

EXAM TIPS

Always try to illustrate your answer with case studies, even when the question does not specifically ask for them. In this case, you have the opportunity to use examples of tropical storms and volcanic eruptions. Make sure that you are careful and only refer to the hazards that are required in the question – in this case tropical storms in part (a), and volcanic eruptions in part (b). It could be useful to use a highlighter pen to highlight key terms such as *volcanic eruption* and *tropical storm,* to make sure that your answer has the right focus.

Agricultural systems

7

1 How do natural and human inputs influence the processes and outputs of agricultural systems?

Farming systems and types

Farming is an industry and operates like other industries. It is a **system** with **inputs** into the farm, **processes** which take place on the farm and **outputs** from the farm (Figure 7.1).

KEY QUESTIONS

1 How do natural and human inputs influence the processes and outputs of agricultural systems?

2 What are the causes and effects of, and possible solutions to, food shortages?

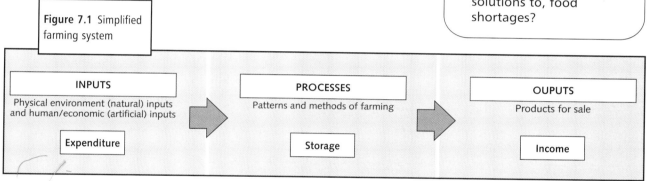

Figure 7.1 Simplified farming system

INPUTS	PROCESSES	OUPUTS
Physical environment (natural) inputs and human/economic (artificial) inputs	Patterns and methods of farming	Products for sale
Expenditure	Storage	Income

Key words to know

Systems
Inputs
Processes
Outputs

The farmer as a decision maker

Each individual farmer's decision on what crops to grow or animals to rear, and which methods to use to maximise outputs, depends on an understanding of the most favourable physical and economic conditions for the farm (Figure 7.2). Sometimes the farmer may have several choices and so the decision may depend upon individual likes and expertise. On other occasions the choice may be limited by extreme physical conditions or economic and political pressures. Figure 7.3 shows how farming systems vary between more economically developed countries (MEDCs) and less economically developed countries (LEDCs).

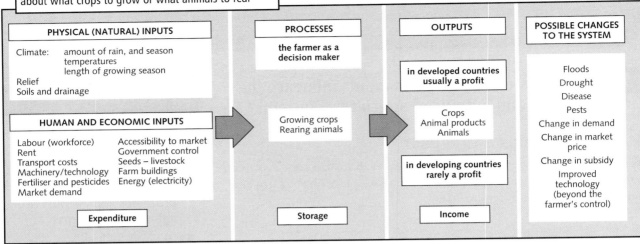

Figure 7.2 Factors affecting the farmer's decision about what crops to grow or what animals to rear

PHYSICAL (NATURAL) INPUTS

Climate: amount of rain, and season
temperatures
length of growing season
Relief
Soils and drainage

HUMAN AND ECONOMIC INPUTS

Labour (workforce)   Accessibility to market
Rent   Government control
Transport costs   Seeds – livestock
Machinery/technology   Farm buildings
Fertiliser and pesticides Energy (electricity)
Market demand

Expenditure

PROCESSES

the farmer as a decision maker

Growing crops
Rearing animals

Storage

OUTPUTS

in developed countries usually a profit

Crops
Animal products
Animals

in developing countries rarely a profit

Income

POSSIBLE CHANGES TO THE SYSTEM

Floods
Drought
Disease
Pests
Change in demand
Change in market price
Change in subsidy
Improved technology (beyond the farmer's control)

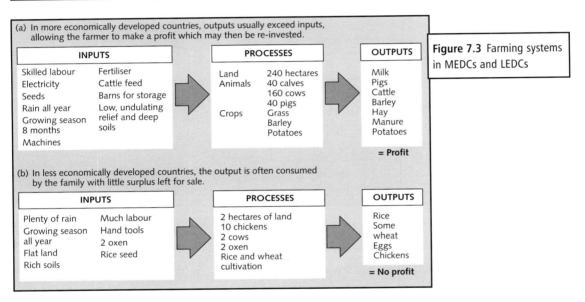

(a) In more economically developed countries, outputs usually exceed inputs, allowing the farmer to make a profit which may then be re-invested.

INPUTS	PROCESSES	OUTPUTS

Skilled labour Fertiliser
Electricity Cattle feed
Seeds Barns for storage
Rain all year Low, undulating
Growing season relief and deep
8 months soils
Machines
	Land 240 hectares
	Animals 40 calves
	  160 cows
	  40 pigs
	Crops Grass
	  Barley
	  Potatoes
		Milk
		Pigs
		Cattle
		Barley
		Hay
		Manure
		Potatoes
		
		= Profit

Figure 7.3 Farming systems in MEDCs and LEDCs

(b) In less economically developed countries, the output is often consumed by the family with little surplus left for sale.

INPUTS	PROCESSES	OUTPUTS
Plenty of rain Much labour Growing season Hand tools all year 2 oxen Flat land Rice seed Rich soils	2 hectares of land 10 chickens 2 cows 2 oxen Rice and wheat cultivation	Rice Some wheat Eggs Chickens = No profit

Back to ...

The New Wider World **p97** for more information about the classification of types of farming.

Classification of farming types

Figure 7.4 shows the main types of farming. Remember that the map is simplified. It only shows the generalised world location of the main types of farming. It does not show local variations or transitions between the main farming types, and it does not show where several types occur within the same area.

Check this!...

1 Name any two natural or physical inputs into a farming system.

2 Name any two human or economic inputs.

3 How do you think the relative importance of natural and human inputs will vary between MEDCs and LEDCs?

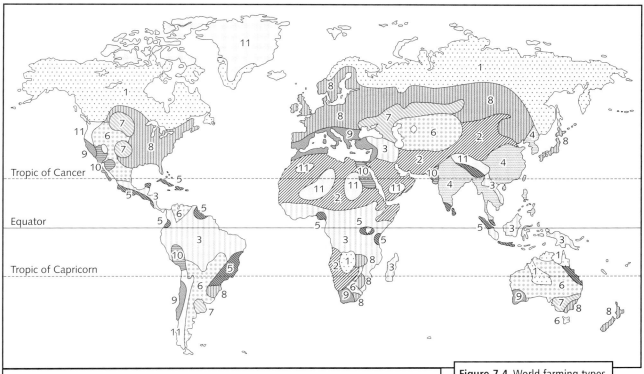

Figure 7.4 World farming types

Type of farming	Named example
1 Nomadic hunting and collecting	Australian aborigines
2 Nomadic herding	Maasai in Kenya, Sahel countries
3 Shifting cultivation	Amerindians of Amazon basin
4 Intensive subsistence agriculture	Rice in the Ganges delta
5 Plantation agriculture	Sugar cane in Brazil
6 Livestock ranching (commercial pastoral)	Beef on the Pampas
7 Cereal cultivation (commercial grain)	Canadian Prairies, Russian Steppes
8 Mixed farming	Netherlands, Denmark
9 'Mediterranean' agriculture	Southern Italy, southern Spain
10 Irrigation	Nile valley, California
11 Unsuitable for agriculture	Sahara Desert

Examples of agricultural systems

Plantation agriculture

A **plantation** is a large farm that is generally located in tropical or sub-tropical regions. Plantation agriculture is usually now associated with LEDCs. In the past, however, plantations were self-contained estates in the Americas, including the USA, where crops such as cotton and tobacco were planted and grown by slave labour.

Characteristics of plantations include their size (they are larger than local farms), and that generally only one crop is cultivated – a system called **monoculture.** Most crops grown on plantations are grown for export to MEDCs, as the climate is not suitable for their growth in these countries. This is called the cultivation of **cash crops.** Typical cash crops include sugar cane, coffee, tea, cocoa, rubber and bananas.

Plantations are often owned by **transnational corporations** – large companies which have factories and offices in several countries. These take most of the profit back to MEDCs. The transnationals own the land on which the crops are grown, employ the local labour, and control production right through to the sale of the product in an MEDC. The large-scale control of the farming process is called **agribusiness.**

Key words to know

Plantation
Monoculture
Cash crops
Transnational corporations
Agribusinesses

Plantations can use up valuable farmland that cannot then be used by local farmers. They are therefore often seen as exploiting the local population. However, there are some benefits associated with this type of agriculture. For example, it can provide a higher standard of living for plantation workers than they would have as subsistence farmers. They may be provided with facilities such as housing, education, health care, and shops.

Brazilian coffee

Coffee is an evergreen tree that is native to Africa. Of the three types of coffee grown commercially, the Arabica tree is widely cultivated in Central and South America, particularly in Brazil. Coffee is grown in tropical regions, but at an altitude high enough for temperatures to be between 13 and 26 °C (so not too hot). The soil needs to be rich, fertile and absorbent, and yet fairly freely draining.

Brazil is the world's leading producer of coffee. Much of the crop is grown on large plantations. Many of these plantations are owned by transnational corporations, such as Nestlé. About one-quarter of the world's coffee is grown on the plantations around São Paulo, Paraná, Espírito Santo, and Minas Gerais. Annual coffee production in 2002 was about 2.39 million tonnes, much of which was exported.

Subsistence agriculture

Case Study

Subsistence rice farming in the Lower Ganges Valley

Back to ...

The New Wider World **pp112–113** for the case study of subsistence rice farming in the Lower Ganges Valley.

Using your case study

Use this case study to answer questions on agricultural systems, especially on small-scale subsistence farming. You will need to relate your answer to the systems shown in Figures 7.1–7.3. You also need to know:
- the location of the Lower River Ganges
- the physical inputs into this system
- the human inputs into this system
- the processes
- the outputs
- ways in which this system has changed recently, including the impact of the Green Revolution (see also pages 75–76 of this *Coursemate*).

Update

Go to *The NWW Coursemates* website for a link to 'Banglapedia', which has information about all aspects of life in Bangladesh.

Learn it!

1 Describe the location of the Lower Ganges Valley.

2 What is a 'subsistence farmer'?

3 Draw a systems diagram similar to Figure 7.3b to show the inputs, processes and outputs of this system.

4 Explain how recent changes have affected the system. How do you think these changes have benefited all farmers in the region?

2 What are the causes and effects of, and possible solutions to, food shortages?

Food supply and malnutrition

Global food production has increased since the 1960s (except in Africa where there has been a 10 per cent decrease). This means that there has been a fall in the *proportion* of underfed people. However, because world population and poverty have increased, the actual *number* of people suffering from **malnutrition** has also increased.

Malnutrition is caused by deficiencies in diet, either in amount (quantity) or type (quality). Until the 1970s, it was believed that malnutrition resulted from the population growing more rapidly than food supplies could be increased. Today, though, it is attributed to poverty, because many people around the world cannot afford to buy an adequate diet. Malnutrition only results in starvation in extreme conditions, but many people find it difficult to work, and have little resistance to disease, when they are malnourished. It can retard the mental and physical development of children, and makes them vulnerable to disease.

Dietary energy supply (DES)

Dietary energy supply, or DES, is the number of calories per capita (that is, per person) available each day in a country. It does not take into account differences between individuals or between areas within a country. Between 1970 and 2000 there was an increase in available food supplies per capita in every developing region except sub-Saharan Africa. It has been estimated that in most LEDCs, especially those within the tropics, a person consuming less than 2350 calories per day is likely to experience chronic malnutrition (Figure 7.5). In 2000, 20 per cent of people living in these countries were suffering from chronic malnutrition. Their numbers increased from 435 million in 1975 to 600 million in 2000. This increase is mainly due to human factors (for example civil wars, political instability and international debt) rather than to physical causes (for example a natural disaster such as drought).

Key word to know
Malnutrition

Back to ...
The New Wider World **p110** Figure 7.35 and **p77** Figure 7.8 in this *Coursemate* for a map showing world dietary energy supply.

Region	1970	1980	1990	2000
Sub-Saharan Africa	35	36	37	42
Near East and North Africa	23	10	5	12
Central America and Caribbean	24	15	13	11
South America	17	12	12	9
South Asia	34	30	24	22
East Asia	35	22	17	16
China	46	28	16	14
All developing regions	36	26	20	19

Figure 7.5 Percentage of chronically underfed people, 1970–2000

People living in MEDCs need more calories per day than those in LEDCs. This is partly because there is a greater proportion of adults in MEDCs (children have smaller needs) and partly because most MEDCs are in cooler latitudes (where more energy is needed to keep the body warm).

Malnutrition in children

Children under the age of 5 are particularly likely to suffer from malnutrition. In 2000, 35 per cent of children in this age-group in LEDCs were considered to be underweight (Figure 7.6). Surprisingly the percentage is highest in South-east Asia where, despite improvements in food supply per capita since 1970 (Figure 7.5), 78 per cent of the developing world's underweight children live. In contrast, Africa has only 15 per cent of the total underweight children (Figure 7.6).

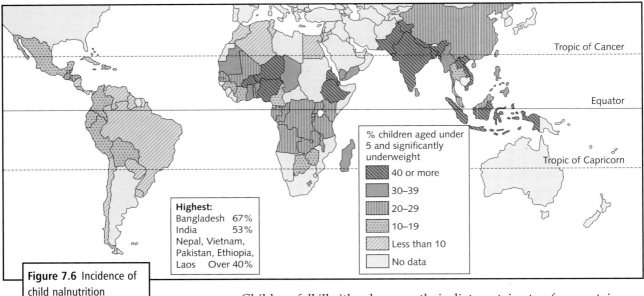

Highest:
Bangladesh 67%
India 53%
Nepal, Vietnam,
Pakistan, Ethiopia,
Laos Over 40%

% children aged under 5 and significantly underweight
- 40 or more
- 30–39
- 20–29
- 10–19
- Less than 10
- No data

Figure 7.6 Incidence of child nalnutrition

Children fall ill either because their diet contains too few proteins, which are particularly important during early stages of growth, or too few calories.

- The two major protein deficiency diseases are marasmus and kwashiorkor. *Marasmus* is most common in children in their first year of life. *Kwashiorkor* results from a predominance of cereals (e.g. rice) and a deficiency of protein (e.g. milk, eggs and meat).
- Two of several diseases resulting from a lack of vitamins are beri-beri and rickets. *Beri-beri*, due to a lack of vitamin B, can lead to a wasting and paralysis of limbs. *Rickets*, caused by a deficiency in vitamin D, causes deformities in bones, legs and the spine.

Why do some people in sub-Saharan Africa suffer from malnutrition?

- The high birth rate and falling death rate means there are many more people to be fed.
- Few farmers have the money to buy high-yielding seeds, fertiliser, pesticides or machinery, or to implement irrigation schemes, to help them grow more food crops.
- When food is scarce, neither governments nor people can afford to buy high-priced goods from overseas.
- During colonial times, European companies established commercial crops for their own profit instead of encouraging subsistence crops for local use. Although they are now independent, the governments of some countries still give tax concessions to overseas transnationals, allowing them to continue to grow these crops.

- The soil has been overused in the past and few nutrients remain. In places soil erosion has led to desertification.
- Many areas receive small and unreliable amounts of rainfall.
- Pests and diseases destroy crops and stored grain.
- Often there is not enough protein in the diet.
- In many countries there is political instability.

Possible solutions to food shortages

The Green Revolution

The Green Revolution refers to the application of modern, Western-type farming techniques to LEDCs. It began with the development of high-yielding varieties (HYVs) of cereals – new varieties of maize and wheat in Mexico and rice in the Philippines (the rice increased yields by 6 per cent in the first year). Although the new seeds were faster growing and disease resistant, they needed large amounts of fertiliser and pesticides, making farming less *sustainable*.

Figure 7.7 Successes and failures of the Green Revolution

Successes

- HYVs have increased food production. For example, India used to experience food shortages until the 1960s, when it became self-sufficient in cereals.
- The increase in yields led to a fall in food prices.
- Faster-growing varieties allow an extra crop to be grown each year.
- Yields are more reliable as many new varieties are more disease-resistant.
- Higher yields allow other crops, notably vegetables, to be grown, adding variety to the local diet.
- HYVs allow the production of some commercial crops.
- HYVs are not so tall as traditional varieties, so they are better able to withstand wind and rain.
- Many of the more well-off farmers who could afford seed, fertiliser and tractors, have become richer.

Failures

- HYVs need large amounts of fertiliser and pesticides which increase costs, encourage the growth of weeds and can harm water supplies.
- HYVs need a more reliable and controlled supply of water. They are more vulnerable to drought and to waterlogging. Irrigation, where it is used, increases costs and can cause salinisation.
- HYVs are more susceptible to attacks by pests and diseases.
- Many of the poorer farmers who do not own the land they farm and cannot afford to buy seed, fertiliser and tractors, have become much poorer.
- Mechanisation has increased rural unemployment and migration to the towns.
- Farming has become less sustainable.

Intermediate technology solutions

Large-scale solutions such as the Green Revolution have had a major impact, but as seen in Figure 7.7 they may have drawbacks and not benefit all farmers. It is important that there are also smaller-scale, sustainable solutions to the problem.

This is where **intermediate technology** is important. This is the use of often small-scale solutions using materials and expertise appropriate to the problem, rather than expensive, high-tech solutions that may fail. In India, for example, 230 000 villages in 1980 were classified as being

Back to ...

The New Wider World p256 and p68 of this *Coursemate* for information about desertification; pp224 and 256 for information about problems caused by insufficient or unreliable rainfall.

Check this!...

1 Explain what is meant by each of the following:
   a) plantations
   b) monoculture
   c) cash crops
   d) agribusiness.

2 Give one benefit and one disadvantage of plantation agriculture for a nation's economy.

3 What is malnutrition?

4 Describe and explain the distribution of regions where malnutrition is a particular problem.

5 Explain why malnutrition is such a severe problem in sub-Saharan Africa.

Back to ...

The New Wider World p108 for information on the effects of chemicals on water supplies.

Back to ...

The New Wider World p109 Figure 7.33 for a diagram showing how salinisation occurs.

Key words to know

Intermediate technology

1 What is the Green Revolution?

2 Evaluate the successes and failures of the Green Revolution. Overall, do you think the Green Revolution has provided a solution to the problems of food shortages in some parts of the world?

3 What is 'intermediate technology'?

4 Using an example, explain how intermediate technology may be an appropriate solution to problems in LEDCs.

'water problem villages'. This meant that they were more than 1.6 km from a water supply. Rather than the building of costly dams and lengthy networks of piping, a smaller-scale solution to this problem is to provide cheap local electric pumps that are able to retrieve water from beneath the surface.

In Nepal, the clearance of forests on the slopes of the Himalayas has led to soil erosion problems in Nepal, and also to more frequent flooding downstream in Bangladesh. A solution to this problem is to maintain a network of small terraces, growing rice on the lower irrigated slopes, and maize and millet which rely on natural rainfall on higher slopes. Farmers have also planted fast-growing pine trees here to help prevent further soil erosion.

EXAM PRACTICE

a Look at Figure 7.1, which shows a simplified farming system.

   i Name one natural input to a farming system. (1)

   ii How might the outputs of a farming system differ between MEDCs and LEDCs? (2)

b Look at Figure 7.8, which shows dietary energy supply.

   i Explain what is meant by the term 'dietary energy supply'. (3)

   ii Describe the pattern shown on Figure 7.8. (4)

   iii Do you think dietary energy supply is a good measure of a country's state of development? Explain your answer. (3)

c i Explain how either of the following may help to solve the problem of food shortages in some parts of the world:

      • food aid

      • the Green Revolution. (5)

   ii With reference to an economic activity that you have studied, explain the inputs, processes and outputs that contribute to the way the system works. (7)

Figure 7.8 World dietary energy supply

Tropic of Cancer

Equator

Tropic of Capricorn

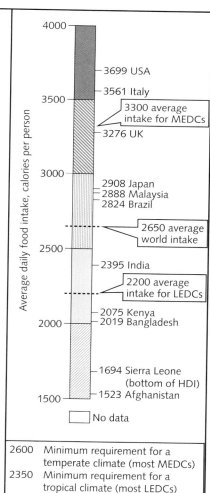

Average daily food intake, calories per person

- 4000
- 3699 USA
- 3561 Italy
- 3300 average intake for MEDCs
- 3500
- 3276 UK
- 3000
- 2908 Japan
- 2888 Malaysia
- 2824 Brazil
- 2650 average world intake
- 2500
- 2395 India
- 2200 average intake for LEDCs
- 2075 Kenya
- 2019 Bangladesh
- 2000
- 1694 Sierra Leone (bottom of HDI)
- 1523 Afghanistan
- 1500

☐ No data

2600	Minimum requirement for a temperate climate (most MEDCs)
2350	Minimum requirement for a tropical climate (most LEDCs)

EXAM TIPS

This is an example of a question where one part (usually the last) carries a large proportion of the total marks available. Make sure, when you are looking through the question, that you are aware of the number of marks available for each part, and that you spend an appropriate amount of time on each.

In question (c), there are two other points worth noting:

- This is an example of a question where it could be useful to provide a diagram to help explain your answer, in this case a systems diagram.

- Notice that the question requires you to refer to *an economic activity that you have studied*. This does not necessarily have to be agriculture, but could be a manufacturing or service industry – as long as you use a specific named example.

Back to …

The NWW Coursemates website to check your answers to the exam practice question.

⇨ *The New Wider World*, pp92; 94; 96; 136–137; 140; 145; 147; 152–155; 180–181

KEY QUESTIONS

1 How is industry classified?

2 How does employment structure differ in MEDCs and LEDCs?

3 What inputs influence the processes and outputs of industrial systems?

4 What factors influence the distribution of high-technology and manufacturing industries?

1 How is industry classified?

Classification of economic activities

Traditionally, industry and other types of **economic activity** are broken down into the main groups of **primary, secondary** and **tertiary** industries.

- **Primary** industries extract raw materials directly from the earth or sea. Examples include farming, fishing, forestry and mining.
- **Secondary** industries process and manufacture the primary products, for example steelmaking and furniture manufacture. They also include the construction industry and the assembly of components made by other secondary industries, for example car assembly.
- **Tertiary** industries provide a service. These include education, health, office work, retailing, transport and entertainment.

Employment structure

The proportion of people working in each of the primary, secondary and tertiary sectors is called the **employment structure**. The figure for each group is given as a percentage of the total. Employment structures change over a period of time and vary from place to place.

Back to ...

The New Wider World **p92** Figure 6.1 for some examples of people working in the different sectors of employment.

Key words to know

Economic activity
Primary industries
Secondary industries
Tertiary industries
Employment structure

Back to ...

The New Wider World **p92** Figure 6.2 for pie-graphs showing how employment structure has changed over the last 200 years in the United Kingdom, a typical MEDC.

Back to ...

The New Wider World **pp180–181** for information on differences in development between countries and regions.

2 How does employment structure differ in MEDCs and LEDCs?

Employment structures and development

Usually there is a link between employment structures and levels of economic development of countries, or regions.

As shown on Figure 8.1:

- The richer, industrialised more economically developed countries (MEDCs) have a very high percentage in the tertiary sector, a high percentage in the secondary sector and a very low percentage in the primary sector. Primary industries such as farming and mining have become mechanised and efficient. They therefore employ relatively few people. This enables more people to work in the secondary and tertiary sectors.
- In contrast, the poorer, least industrialised less economically developed countries (LEDCs) have a very high percentage in the primary sector (most are farmers), and a low percentage in both the secondary and service sectors. Farming in many LEDCs is not mechanised or efficient, and so it employs many people. This means that fewer people are available to work in the secondary or tertiary sectors.

- Some countries have industrialised rapidly, such as Brazil and Malaysia. Although they still have a relatively high proportion of their population employed in primary industry, the secondary and tertiary sectors in these countries are expanding quickly. These are known as **newly industrialised countries (NICs)**.

Key words to know

Newly industrialised countries (NICs)

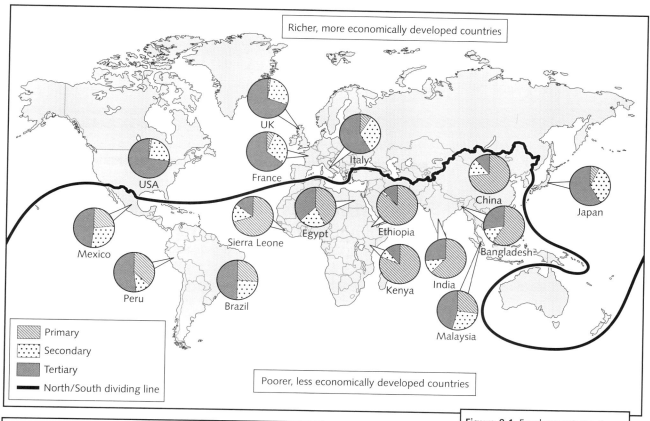

Figure 8.1 Employment structures and economic development

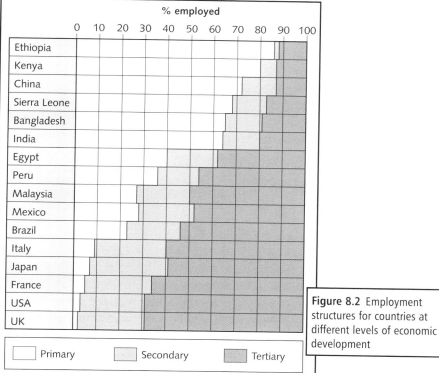

Figure 8.2 Employment structures for countries at different levels of economic development

Back to ...

The New Wider World **p147** for more information about NICs, and about Malaysia as a named example of an NIC.

Figure 8.2 ranks a selection of countries according to the proportion of people engaged in the primary sector.

Back to ...

The New Wider World
p96, and **p69** in this *Coursemate*, for the farming system.

Key words to know

System
Inputs
Processes
Outputs

3 What inputs influence the processes and outputs of industrial systems?

Industry as a whole, or individual factories, can be regarded as a **system**. At its simplest, there are **inputs** into a factory (or industry), **processes** that take place in the factory, and **outputs** from the factory (Figure 8.3). If a firm is to be profitable and to remain in business, the value of its outputs must be greater than the cost of its inputs. Some of the profit should then be re-invested, for example in modernising the factory and introducing new technology.

Figure 8.3 The industrial system

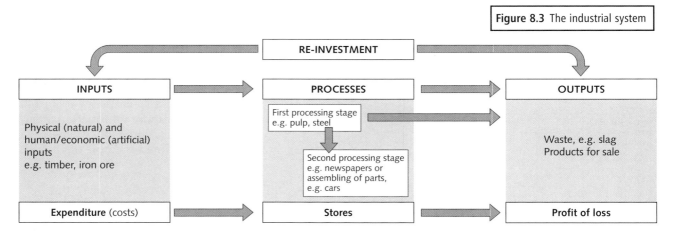

Factors affecting the location of industry

Key words to know

Nationalised company
Transnational corporation (TNC)

Factories may be built by individuals, by a private firm, a nationalised company or a transnational corporation. A **nationalised company** is one that is owned by the government of a country. A **transnational corporation (TNC)** is a company that operates in more than one country, usually with its headquarters in an MEDC. Most of the world's TNCs are based either in Japan or the USA.

Before a factory is built, decisions have to be made about the site for its location. It is unlikely that any site will have all the factors that are listed as advantages in Figure 8.4. Where several sites are available, the individual or company must decide which is likely to provide the best location. Often this decision is determined by predicting which site will give the greatest profit. This will be where the costs of raw materials, land, energy, labour and transport are minimised and where there is a large market for the product. The decision may also be affected by government policies.

Check this!...

1 Make a copy of Figure 8.3. Add labels to your diagram to show how one manufacturing industry of your choice fits that model.

2 a) Use one colour to highlight all natural or physical inputs into your chosen industry.

 b) Use a second colour to highlight the human and economic factors.

3 Which are more important on your completed diagram? Why do you think this is the case?

4 What similarities and differences do you think there are between a system for a manufacturing industry and a farming system?

5 What is a transnational corporation? Name three TNCs operating in your country. In which country is each of the corporation headquarters based?

Figure 8.4 Some factors affecting the location of industry

Physical factors

Raw materials The bulkier and heavier these are to transport, the nearer the factory should be located to the raw materials.

Power – energy This is needed to work the machines in a factory. Early industry needed to be sited near to fast-flowing rivers or coal reserves, but today electricity can be transported long distances.

Natural routes River valleys and flat areas were essential in the days before the railway, car or lorry.

Site and land Some industries, e.g. large-scale manufacturing industries, need large areas of flat land. Many industries have moved from cities to places where land is cheaper and more easily available.

Human and economic factors

Labour This includes both quantity and quality (some areas demand special skills as technology develops).

Capital (money) Banks and governments provide most of the money.

Markets The size and location of markets have become more important than the source of raw materials.

Transport Costs increase when items to be moved are bulky, fragile, heavy or perishable.

Economies of scale Small units may be unprofitable and so merge with, or are taken over by, other firms.

Government policies As governments tend to control most wealth, they can influence industrial location.

Improved technology Examples are facsimile (fax) machines and electronic mail.

Case Study

Industry in a city in a developed country – Osaka–Kobe, Japan

Back to ...

The New Wider World **pp152–153** for the case study of industry in Osaka–Kobe.

Using your case study

Use this case study to answer questions on industrial systems. You should:
- explain why Osaka–Kobe became a focus for industrial development
- give named examples of industries located in the area.

Update

Go to *The NWW Coursemates* website for a link giving information on all aspects of Kobe city.

Learn it!

1 Describe the reasons why Osaka–Kobe grew to be one of Japan's major industrial centres.

2 Describe the process of manufacturing with reference to at least one named industry in the city.

Industry in a city in a developing country – São Paulo, Brazil

Back to ...

The New Wider World **pp154–155** for the case study of industry in São Paulo.

Using your case study

Use this case study to answer questions on industrial systems. You should:

- explain why São Paulo grew to be one of Brazil's major industrial centres
- describe the process of manufacturing with reference to at least one named industry in the city.

Update

Go to *The NWW Coursemates* website for a link giving economic data for Brazil.

Learn it!

1 Why did São Paulo grow to become one of Brazil's major industrial centres?

2 Describe some of the benefits that industrial growth has brought to the city.

3 What problems has this growth led to?

4 What factors influence the distribution of high-technology and manufacturing industries?

High-technology industries

The term **high-technology industry** (or high-tech) refers to industries whose processing techniques often involve micro-electronics. These industries have mostly developed, very rapidly, within the last 25 years. They employ fewer people than the older, declining heavy industries. Two subdivisions of high-tech industries are:

- the 'sunrise industries' which have a high-technology base
- information technology industries involving computers, telecommunications and micro-electronics.

A very skilled, inventive, intelligent workforce is essential. Access to raw materials is relatively unimportant. They are described as **footloose industries** because they can locate almost anywhere. Unlike manufacturing industries, they do not have to be close to any raw materials. So high-tech industries tend to locate in places which the researchers and operators find attractive – from a climatic, scenic, health and social point of view.

Back to ...

The New Wider World **p137** for examples of footloose industries; **p140** for examples of high-technology industries; and **p141** for information on Tsukuba Science City near Tokyo.

Key words to know

High-technology industry (high-tech)
Footloose industries

Case Study Extra

Compaq computer corporation

Compaq is a transnational corporation selling personal and business computers. The headquarters of the company is in Texas, in the USA.

Compaq was founded in 1982. The company rapidly gained a reputation as a manufacturer of high-quality, relatively expensive computers sold through exclusive dealers. Most of its initial business was directed at large corporations. Within six years, sales of Compaq computers exceeded $2 billion.

By the late 1980s, new manufacturers of computers began selling them at lower prices, undercutting Compaq. In response to this,

Compaq began selling computers at lower prices, built more cheaply, to a wider range of distributors throughout the world.

In 2001 Compaq merged with Hewlett Packard to become a high-tech giant to rival IBM, the world's leading computer company.

Using your case study

Use this case study to answer questions on industrial systems. You will need to know:

- how Compaq began
- how it developed in response to the changing market for computers
- how the company is set for the future.

Update

Go to *The NWW Coursemates* website for a link to Compaq giving information about all aspects of the devleopment and status of the corporation.

Learn it!

1 How did Compaq initially build and sell its computers?

2 Why did the company have to adapt in the 1980s? How did it do this?

3 What has the company done recently to expand its business?

Manufacturing industries

The global car industry – a manufacturing industry

Most car firms have factories in many countries. They are transnational corporations (TNCs). They found that by locating in different parts of the world they could:

- avoid having to pay to import cars into other countries (some countries impose charges on imports, in order to protect their own markets – these charges are known as **tariffs**, or **trade barriers**)
- reduce costs by using the cheaper local labour and/or raw materials
- be nearer to large markets (centres of population).

Ford – a global car corporation

The term **globalisation** is used to describe those TNCs that see the world, rather than the local area, as their supplier of labour, raw materials and component parts, and as their area of sales. They have created a world market for their products.

The giant Ford Corporation was originally located in Detroit. A hundred years later, by the late 1990s, it had changed.

- It was manufacturing and/or assembling its cars worldwide, although most of the parts were still produced in the more industrialised parts of North America, Japan and the EU.
- It was increasingly locating its new factories in LEDCs – these either manufactured cars (e.g. in São Paulo) or assembled parts that were made somewhere else (e.g. in Malaysia and the Philippines).
- Parts were now made in several countries, so each model of car was no longer made in one country.
- Ford faced increased competition, especially from Japanese manufacturers. The 1900s was a period of economic recession. Any factory closures were more likely in the LEDCs where the local market is smaller. Also, the parent company was less concerned about people in those countries losing their jobs.
- In Detroit, Ford was working with its previous rivals, Chrysler and General Motors, to produce a car that uses less fuel, causes less pollution and challenges competition from Japanese and Korean car manufacturers.

Key words to know

Tariffs
Trade barriers
Globalisation

Back to ...

The New Wider World **p145**
Figure 9.20 for a map showing the worldwide production and assembly of Ford cars.

Back to ...

The New Wider World **p145**
Figure 9.23 for a photograph
of Ford's car plant in Detroit.

Check this!...

1 What is 'high-technology industry'?

2 What is a 'footloose industry'?

3 Why did car firms choose to locate in different parts of the world?

4 Describe the growth and development of the Ford motor company.

5 Draw a diagram of a large factory. Add labels to your diagram to show how the Ford motor company fits that industrial system.

Detroit – motor city

Henry Ford, a local man, saw Detroit as an ideal location for what was to become the world's first mass-production line. He built his factory on flat land next to the Detroit River, at the heart of the Great Lakes waterway system. Steel was produced on a site nearby, using relatively local iron ore (brought by ship) and coal (brought by train). Ford developed a large local market by paying his workers $5 a day, when the national average was $9 a week, so they were able to buy their own cars. The high wages attracted workers from all over the world, especially from the south-east of the USA. Later, America's two other car giants, Chrysler and General Motors, also located their main factories at Detroit. After a serious depression in the 1970s (which was due to the world oil crisis and competition from Japan), Detroit's car industry is again thriving.

EXAM PRACTICE

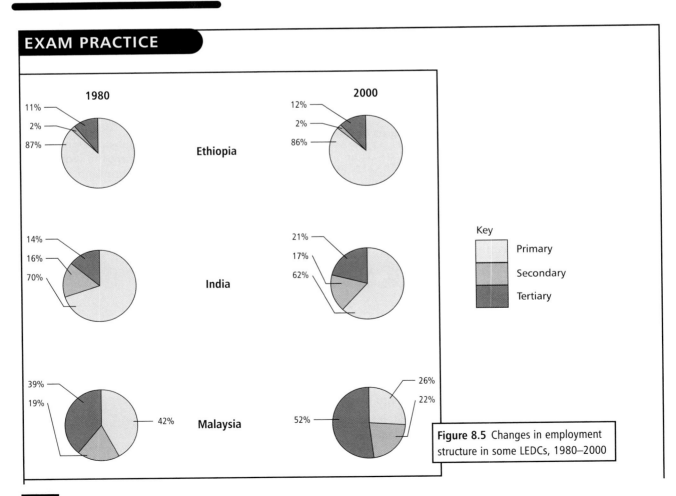

Figure 8.5 Changes in employment structure in some LEDCs, 1980–2000

a Look at Figure 8.5.

   i How does the percentage employment in primary industries vary between the three countries? (1)

   ii Why do these differences exist? (2)

   iii What changes took place between 1980 and 2000? (3)

   iv Suggest reasons for these changes. (4)

b Look at Figure 8.2, which shows employment structures for several countries. Use the diagram to help you with these questions.

   i How would you expect a pie graph showing employment for an MEDC to differ from the general structure shown by the pie graphs in Figure 8.5? (3)

   ii With reference to your answer to (a) (iv), explain these differences. (5)

c For *either* high-technology industries *or* a named manufacturing industry, describe and explain the factors that influenced its growth at a named location you have studied. (7)

EXAM TIPS

Make sure that you provide exactly what the question is asking for. Look at questions (a) (i) and (ii) above. The first part of the question is asking you to *describe* the pie charts. Part (ii) asks you to give *reasons* for the differences. You will not lose any marks for giving explanations in part (i), but you will waste time – and this is one thing you do not have much of in the exam!

Look for the key words in each question. This is the word (or words) that tell you what you need to do. The most common are words like *describe*, *explain*, and the simple *what, why, where* questions. Take a highlighter pen into the exam with you, and highlight the key words in each question before you answer it.

Back to …

The NWW Coursemates website to check your answers to the exam practice question.

⇨ *The New Wider World*, pp160; 164; 166–171; 221

KEY QUESTIONS

1 Why has tourism grown to be such an important global industry?

2 What are the benefits and disadvantages of tourism?

Key words to know

Globalisation
Mass tourism

1 Why has tourism grown to be such an important global industry?

Tourism has become the world's fastest-growing and largest industry. It is an important factor in the economy of most more economically developed countries (MEDCs). It is seen by many less economically developed countries (LEDCs) as the best way to obtain income, create jobs and to improve their standard of living. It has grown rapidly in the last 50 years, mainly as a result of **globalisation** – which in this context means the easier movement of people around the world.

In 1950, 25 million 'international arrivals' were recorded worldwide. By 1975 this figure had risen to 225 million, and 700 million by 2000. Even so, this figure is small compared with the number of 'domestic' tourists – people who travel within their own countries. Travel for just a few rich people has been replaced by **mass tourism**.

Figure 9.1 shows that MEDCs receive just over 75 per cent of all international tourist arrivals. However, their share has fallen from 82 per cent in 1980 as destinations in LEDCs in Africa, South-east Asia, the Pacific and the Middle East have become more popular and accessible.

Recent trends in tourism, and the changing demands made by tourists, have resulted from a wide range of factors. These factors include:

- an increase in wealth, mobility and accessibility
- improvements in transport and technology
- changes in life-styles, interests and demands
- a greater awareness of places due to coverage by the media and TV.

Figure 9.2 is a summary of some of the factors that explain why tourism is an important global industry.

Figure 9.1 International tourist arrivals by region

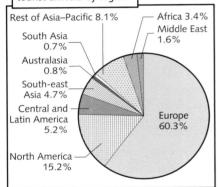

Rest of Asia–Pacific 8.1%
South Asia 0.7%
Australasia 0.8%
South-east Asia 4.7%
Central and Latin America 5.2%
North America 15.2%
Africa 3.4%
Middle East 1.6%
Europe 60.3%

Figure 9.2 Factors affecting the development of tourism as a global industry

Factors	Specific examples	World example
1 Transport and accessibility	● Railways ● Car and coach ● Plane ● Cruise ships	Paris, Istanbul (Orient Express) Rhinelands, Alps Florida, Ayers Rock (Uluru) Norwegian fiords, Caribbean
2 Scenery	● Sandy beaches ● Coasts of outstanding beauty ● Mountains, lakes and rivers	Benidorm, Rio de Janeiro Great Barrier Reef Nepal (Mount Everest), South Africa (Table Mountain), China (Guilin Gorge)
3 Weather	● Hot, dry, sunny summers ● Snow	Costa del Sol, Greece Alps, Rockies
4 Accommodation	● Hotels, resorts ● Holiday camps ● Caravan parks and campsites	Benidorm, Costa del Sol Caribbean French Riviera
5 Amenities	● Culture and history (castles, cathedrals) ● Active amenities (sailing, golf, water-skiing) ● Passive amenities (shops, cinemas) ● Theatres, museums, music	Athens, Florence, Paris Costa del Sol, most resorts Disney World Paris, Vienna
6 Ecotourism and sustainability	● Nature reserves and game parks ● World Heritage Sites	Kenya Cairo, Venice, Grand Canyon

Check this!...

1 Why has tourism grown so rapidly in recent years?

2 What is mass tourism?

3 a) Using Figure 9.2, list the factors affecting the development of the tourist industry. Use one colour to highlight natural attractions, and another for those built by people.

b) Why do you think such attractions are more important for tourists on a global scale?

4 What attracts people to visit your own country?

2 What are the benefits and disadvantages of tourism?

Over 60 per cent of holidays are taken to destinations in Europe (Figure 9.1). Two of the most popular types of holiday taken in Europe are winter ski-ing holidays, and coastal resort **package holidays**. For the package holidays, people buy an 'all-in package' which includes travel and accommodation.

Key words to know

Package holidays

Back to ...

The New Wider World **p165** Figure 10.16 for a photograph of Torremolinos, a town on Spain's Costa del Sol.

The New Wider World **pp164–165** for more information on the Costa del Sol.

Coastal resorts – the Costa del Sol, Spain

The Costa del Sol (the sun coast) is the most southerly of Spain's many tourist coasts (*costas*). It faces the sun, the Mediterranean Sea and North Africa. In the 1950s the area was important only for farming and fishing. Since then, both the landscape and the lives of local people have been transformed by tourism.

Figure 9.3 on page 88 shows some of the effects of the growth of tourism on the Costa del Sol.

Winter ski-ing, Courmayeur (Italy)

The mountaineering and winter sports resort of Courmayeur is located in the extreme north-west of Italy. It lies at the foot of Mont Blanc, the highest mountain in Europe. It is also close to where the main road linking Turin in Italy, and France, passes through the Mont Blanc tunnel. Tourism has brought both benefits and problems to the area (Figure 9.4).

Figure 9.3 Social, economic and environmental effects of tourism

	Stage 1 The traditional society	Stage 2 Take-off and development	Stage 3 Peak growth	Stage 4 Stagnation	Stage 5 Rejuvenation? or Decline?
Date	1960s	1970	1980s	1990s	2000s
Social effects					
Tourists from UK to Spain	1960 = 0.4 million	1971 = 3.0 million	1984 = 6.2 million 1988 = 7.5 million	1990 = 7.5 million	
State of, and changes in, tourism	Very few tourists.	Rapid increase in tourism. Government encouragement.	Full capacity reached – tourist demands outstrip resources, e.g. water supply and sewerage	Decline – world recession, prices too high – cheaper upper-market hotels elsewhere. Beach boredom.	
Holiday accommodation	Limited accomodation, very few hotels and apartments, some holiday cottages.	Large hotels built, more apartment blocks and villas.	More large hotels built, also apartments and luxury villas.	Older hotels looking dirty and run down. Fall in house prices. Only high-class hotels allowed to be built.	
Economic effects					
Local employment	Mainly in farming and fishing.	Construction workers, jobs in hotels, cafés, shops. Decline in farming and fishing.	Many in tourism – up to 70% in some areas.	Unemployment increases as tourism declines (30%). Farmers use irrigation.	
Infrastructure (amenities and activities)	Limited access and few amenities. Poor roads. Limited street lighting and electricity.	Some road improvements but congestion in towns. Bars, discos, restaurants and shops added.	E340 opened – 'The Highway of Death'. More congestion in towns. Marinas and golf courses built.	Bars/cafés closing, Malaga by-pass and new air terminal opened.	
Environmental effects					
Landscape and environment	Clean, unspoilt beaches. Warm sea with relatively little pollution. Pleasant villages. Quiet. Little visual pollution.	Farmland built upon. Wildlife frightened away. Beaches and seas less clean.	Mountains hidden by hotels. Litter on beaches. Polluted seas (sewage). Crime (drugs, vandalism and mugging). Noise from traffic and tourism.	Attempts to clean up beaches and seas (EU Blue Flag beaches). New public parks and gardens opened. Nature reserves.	

Figure 9.4 Effects of tourism in Courmayeur

Benefits of tourism
- More and better-paid jobs, especially for younger people.
- Younger people no longer have to leave the area (out-migration) to find work.
- Improved accessibility due to better roads.
- Improved services, including the provision of electricity, a reliable water supply and sewage disposal.
- Leisure amenities added which can be used by local people, e.g. ice-rink, swimming pool.
- Improved shopping.
- The **multiplier effect**, which is when the success of one type of industry – in this case tourism – attracts other forms of economic development and creates more jobs, for example in shops, hotels, restaurants and bars, and also as guides and instructors.

Disadvantages of tourism
- At peak times, tourists outnumber the local population.
- The traditional village is swamped by new buildings, e.g. hotels, chalets, souvenir shops, restaurants, car parks.
- Many of these new buildings, together with ski-lifts and ski-runs, are unsightly and create visual pollution. They spoil the attractive scenery that first attracted tourists.
- The traditional way of life is changed and the local culture is likely to be lost.
- Farmers have lost land and their traditional jobs.
- House prices have risen and become too expensive for local people.
- Unemployment may be seasonal, as many of the jobs are linked to the winter skiing season, e.g. ski-instructors.
- Hillsides are deforested to create new and longer ski-runs. This destroys the fragile alpine ecosystem (vegetation is damaged, wildlife is frightened away) and increases the risk of soil erosion and avalanches.
- The increase in traffic has been blamed for the increase in acid rain that is killing local vegetation.

1 What is a package holiday?

2 Why do so many Europeans take holidays on the Costa del Sol?

3 Describe and explain how the impact of tourism changes through time in a coastal area such as the Costa del Sol.

4 Name three benefits to mountain resorts of tourism.

5 What are some of the disadvantages?

6 In your opinion, do you think it is right to say that the benefits of tourism in countries such as Spain and Italy are greater than the disadvantages? Explain your answer.

Key words to know
Multiplier effect

Back to ...
The New Wider World **pp166–167** for more information on the tourist industry in Courmayeur; *The New Wider World* **p221**, and **pp105–106** of this *Coursemate* for information about the effects of acid rain.

Tourism in developing countries

Since the early 1980s, cheaper flights and better access to a range of destinations have led to a growth of tourism in LEDCs. Many of the most popular destinations are located within, or near to, the tropics (see Figure 9.5) – places such as Kenya, Egypt, Sri Lanka, Thailand, Malaysia and the Caribbean.

The attraction of earning money from tourism is considerable to LEDCs. Many of these countries see it as the only possible way to raise their standard of living. However, only a limited number of LEDCs have the potential to develop a successful tourist industry, and even then the damage to their culture and environment can be greater than the benefits.

Ecotourism

Ecotourism, sometimes known as **green tourism,** is a sustainable form of tourism that is more appropriate to LEDCs than the mass tourism associated with places like Florida and the Spanish costas in MEDCs. Ecotourism includes:

- visiting places in order to appreciate their scenery and wildlife and to understand the local culture
- creating economic opportunities (jobs) in an area while at the same time protecting natural resources (scenery and wildlife) and the local way of life (culture).

Ecotourists usually travel in small groups and share specialist interests (bird watching, photography). They are more likely to merge and live with local communities and to appreciate local cultures rather than 'stop, take a photo and move on'. They often visit National Parks and game reserves where the scenery (e.g. sandy beaches, coral islands, forests and waterfalls) and wildlife (whales, elephants and mountain gorillas) that attracted them there in the first place, are carefully protected and managed.

Even so:

- Most ecotourists pay for their holiday in advance (and therefore spend relatively little in the developing country).
- They are not all educated or concerned about the environment.
- They can cause land prices to rise.
- They tend to congregate at prime sites (honeypots).
- They may still come into conflict with local people.

Key words to know
Ecotourism
Green tourism

Check this!...

1 Why has tourism become important to LEDCs?

2 What is ecotourism?

3 Do you think it is correct to say that ecotourism is a perfect solution to the problems resulting from tourism?

4 a) List three benefits and three disadvantages of tourism in LEDCs.

 b) Now look back to the section on tourism in Spain and Italy (pages 87–88). Do you think LEDCs gain more from tourism, or do you think that richer countries benefit most? Explain your answer.

5 If there is a tourist industry in your country, list the benefits and disadvantages that the industry brings. Do you think that tourism generally is beneficial to your country?

When advertising their holidays, some tour operators add the term 'eco' when that is not an accurate description.

Tourism in the Caribbean

The Caribbean has a number of special attractions to tourists:

- Winters are warm (25°C). Summers are hot (28°C) but not oppressive.
- Most days have more than eight hours of sunshine.
- The scenery is attractive. It is usually either volcanic mountains covered in forest, or coral islands with sandy beaches.
- The warm, clear blue seas are ideal for watersports such as sailing, water-skiing, scuba diving and snorkelling.
- There is varied wildlife – plants, birds, fish and animals.
- Local customs are different – calypsos, steel bands, food, festivals and carnivals.
- There are many cultural and historic resorts.
- The region is situated only a relatively short flight-time from North America.

The *beach village* is a recent attempt to try to disperse accommodation and amenities so that they merge with the natural environment, reduce overcrowding at other places, and avoid spoiling the physical advantages that originally attracted tourists to the islands. Tourism has brought other benefits and problems, too (Figure 9.5).

Figure 9.5 Effects of tourism in the Caribbean

Benefits of tourism
- The natural environment (sun, sand, sea and scenery) attracts tourists and their much-needed money.
- Income from tourism is usually greater than the income from the export of a few raw materials.
- Tourism creates domestic employment, e.g. hotels, entertainment and guides. It is labour intensive.
- It encourages the production of souvenirs.
- It creates a market for local farm produce.
- Local people can use tourist facilities.
- Overseas investment in airports, roads and hotels.
- Profits can be used to improve local housing, schools, hospitals, electricity and water supplies.
- Cultural links with foreign countries are increased and local customs and heritage are preserved.
- Tourism helps to reduce migration.

Disadvantages of tourism
- Hotels, airports and roads spoil the visual appearance and create noise, air pollution and litter.
- Usually only 10–20% of the income received from tourists stays in the country. Most hotels are owned by foreign companies and profits go overseas. Tourists spend most of their money in the hotels.
- Much of the employment is seasonal. Overseas labour may be brought in to fill the better-paid jobs.
- Local craft industries may be destroyed in order to provide mass-produced, cheap souvenirs.
- The farming economy is damaged as land is sold to developers. Much of the food eaten by tourists is imported, either to meet the demands for European-style foods or because local production is insufficient. Prices paid for local products are low.
- Local people cannot afford to use the tourist facilities.
- Money borrowed to provide tourist facilities increases national debt.
- Tourists expect an unlimited supply of water – up to 500 litres a day, or ten times the amount used by local people. Many areas may be short of water for domestic and farming use.
- Local cultures and traditions are destroyed. New social problems of prostitution, crime, drugs and drunkenness are introduced. There is a lack of respect for local customs and religious beliefs (e.g. people dress unsuitably when visiting mosques and temples).
- The building of hotels means that local people lose their homes, land and traditional means of livelihood (e.g. fishermen, as hotels are built next to beaches). These people then become dependent on serving wealthy tourists.

a Look at Figure 9.6. This shows information about safari holidays in Kenya.

Figure 9.6 Safari in Kenya

SAFARIWISE

Safari lodges in Kenya provide all modern comforts. While simple in design, your room will have bath or shower (except Shimba Hills and Treetops where shared facilities are provided) and most lodges have a pool. Cuisine, though not *cordon bleu*, is of good standard and sometimes includes game meat.

We use the best available vehicles – 7- or 9-seater safari cruisers with roof hatches and sliding windows for easy game viewing and photography. Journeys, particularly between game reserves, can be long, dusty and tiring but the excitement of seeing wildlife in its natural habitat usually makes it all worth while. The occasional change in routeing and/or hotels/lodges may be necessary due to weather conditions or shortage of accommodation. Tented accommodation is sometimes included at Samburu or Keekorok – but do not be alarmed! The tents have stand-up room, are heavy-duty and erected on a concrete base under an awning, while to the rear (direct access from tent) are simple but private shower and toilet facilities.

i Why have countries like Kenya become increasingly popular for tourists? (1)

ii What is ecotourism? (2)

iii Give two benefits and one disadvantage of ecotourism. (3)

iv Explain how the safari holiday advertised in Figure 9.6 might

- benefit

- cause problems for

the economy and the natural environment of Kenya. (4)

b Look at Figure 9.2, which shows factors affecting the development of the tourist industry. Use this to help you answer the questions below.

i Explain why tourism has grown to be such an important global industry. (3)

ii What problems might face an area that has been a tourist centre for a long time? (5)

iii With reference to examples you have studied (but *not* ecotourism), explain the benefits and disadvantages that the tourist industry may bring. (7)

Back to …

The New Wider World
pp170–171 for information on how tourism in Kenya affects the environment.

EXAM TIPS

Where a question asks for more than one main point, think carefully about how you set out your answer. For example, look at question (a) (iv) above. This asks you about the natural environment as well as the economy of Kenya. For each part, you need to consider the benefits as well as the disadvantages. In total, this is four main points you have to write about. For this sort of answer, it might be worth drawing a simple table with four boxes in which to write your answers. This will organise your thoughts more clearly – and you could always add something later without it seeming like an afterthought.

Back to …

The NWW Coursemates website to check your answers to the exam practice question.

10

Energy and water resources

➡️ *The New Wider World*, pp119; 120–125; 151; 218; 222–225; 278; 294

KEY QUESTIONS

1 What is the significance of non-renewable and renewable energy?

2 What are the factors that influence the development and siting of different types of power stations?

3 What are the uses, provision and competition for water resources and the impacts of water shortages?

Key words to know

Fossil fuels
Non-renewable resources
Renewable resources

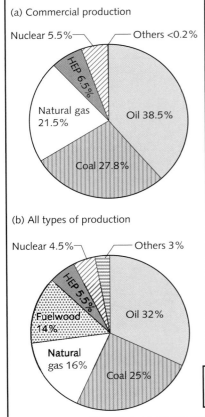

(a) Commercial production

Nuclear 5.5% — Others <0.2%
HEP 6.5%
Natural gas 21.5%
Oil 38.5%
Coal 27.8%

(b) All types of production

Nuclear 4.5% — Others 3%
HEP 5.5%
Fuelwood 14%
Oil 32%
Natural gas 16%
Coal 25%

Figure 10.1 Global energy production

1   What is the significance of non-renewable and renewable energy?

Energy resources

The sun is the primary source of the Earth's energy. Without energy, nothing can live and no work can be done. Green plants convert energy, through the process of photosynthesis, into a form that can be used by people.

Non-renewable resources

In the mid-1990s, coal, oil and natural gas accounted for 87.8 per cent of the world's commercially produced energy (Figure 10.1a). These are forms of stored solar energy produced by photosynthesis in plants over thousands of years. As these three types of energy, referred to as **fossil fuels**, take so long to form and be replaced, they are described as **non-renewable**. Each year the world (mainly the more economically developed countries or MEDCs), consumes an amount of fossil fuel that took nature 1 million years to provide – a rate far greater than their rate of replacement. In the past, fossil fuels have been relatively easy to obtain and cheap to use, but they have become major polluters of the environment.

Two other non-renewable sources of energy are significant. Nuclear energy uses uranium, which is not a fossil fuel. Fuelwood is a non-commercial source of energy. If it is included with the other forms of energy, it provides an estimated 14 per cent of the world's energy requirements and 35 per cent of the needs of LEDCs (Figure 10.1b).

Renewable (alternative) resources

Renewable resources of energy, which are mainly forces of nature which can be used over and over again, are considered to be sustainable. At present only running water (hydro-electricity, or HEP) is a significant source of renewable energy on a global scale (Figure 10.1a). Other sources, which are often more important at a local scale, are the sun (solar), the wind, vegetation waste (biomass) and heat from the Earth (geothermal). Currently, economic and technical problems restrict the conversion of these sources of energy on a large scale. In the future the world is likely to have to look to these and other sources of renewable energy (e.g. waves and tides) as the supply of fossil fuels runs out.

Check this!...

1 Name two fossil fuels.

2 Why are fossil fuels described as 'non-renewable'?

3 Name two renewable sources of energy.

4 Why are renewable energy sources likely to become more important in the future?

Non-renewable energy resources

Coal

Globally, coal production is increasing, although little is used by LEDCs apart from China, which produces and consumes 40 per cent of the world's total.

Advantages
- Reserves are likely to last for over 300 years.
- Improved technology has increased the output per worker, allowed deeper mining with fewer workers, and made conversion to electricity more efficient.
- Coal is used for electricity, heating and making coke. Power stations generate electricity by burning coal, so they are usually located as near as possible to the source of coal, as it is costly to transport.

Disadvantages
- The burning of coal causes air pollution. It releases carbon dioxide, which contributes to global warming.
- Deep mining can be dangerous, while opencast (surface) mining temporarily harms the environment.
- Coal is heavy and bulky to transport.

Oil and natural gas

Many industrialised countries rely on either oil or natural gas as their main source of energy. Very few of them have sufficient reserves of their own.

Advantages
- Oil and gas are more efficient to burn, easier to transport and distribute (by pipeline and tanker), and less harmful to the environment than coal. Gas is even cheaper and cleaner than oil.
- Oil and gas are safer than nuclear energy. Both are used for electricity, with gas increasingly the most favoured of all the non-renewable sources.
- There is greater flexibility in the location of gas-powered power stations, as gas is easier to transport.
- Oil is the basis of the huge petrochemical industry.

Disadvantages
- Reserves may only last another 50–70 years. New fields are increasingly difficult to discover and exploit.
- Terminals and refineries take up much space and there is the danger of spillage (oil), leaks (gas), explosions and fire.
- The burning of gas releases nitrogen oxide, and the burning of oil releases sulphur dioxide. Both of these contribute to acid rain.
- Oil and gas are subject to sudden international price changes and are vulnerable to political, economic and military pressures.

Nuclear energy

Several older industrialised countries (e.g. France and Belgium) and many newly industrialised countries (e.g. Japan, South Korea and Taiwan) lack sufficient fossil fuels of their own, so they have turned increasingly to nuclear power, even though there are fears over its safety.

Advantages
- Only very limited raw materials are needed, e.g. 50 tonnes of uranium per year compared with 540 tonnes of coal per hour needed for coal-fired stations.

Figure 10.21 The advantages and disadvantages of non-renewable resources

Back to ...

The New Wider World **p218** for information on global warming.

Back to ...

The New Wider World **p221** for information about acid rain.

- Oil and natural gas could be exhausted by the year 2030. Coal is difficult to obtain and dirty to use.
- Numerous safeguards make the risks of any accident minimal.
- Nuclear waste is limited and can be stored underground.
- Nuclear energy schemes have the support of large companies and government departments.
- Nuclear power is believed to contribute less than conventional fuels to the greenhouse effect and acid rain.

Disadvantages
- It is not clear how safe it is.
- Many people believe that one accident may kill many people, and ruin an area of ground for hundreds of years.
- Nuclear power cannot be used for two of industry's major demands, heating and transport, as costs are too high.
- In more economically developed countries (MEDCs) there is less demand for energy by industry as declining industries (such as steel) used more energy than those that are replacing them (such as micro-electronics).
- Potential health risks to people who live and work in the area.
- Nuclear waste can remain radioactive for many years. There are problems with reprocessing and then storing nuclear waste.
- The cost of making safe old power stations that are no longer used is extremely high.

Fuelwood

In Africa, trees have been called the 'staff of life' because they are so important in preserving the environment and in providing rural communities with their basic needs (shelter, food, fuel and shade). But in Africa, and in many rural areas in other less economically developed countries (LEDCs), trees are being removed at an ever faster rate. Collecting fuelwood is a time-consuming job for women and children. Each day they may have to walk many kilometres to find enough wood in order to cook their meals (women also have to do the farming and look after large families). Africa's growing population and increasing demand for wood creates a cycle of environmental deprivation.

Back to …

The New Wider World **p121**
Figure 8.9 for a diagram showing the cycle of environmental deprivation.

Key words to know

Thermal power stations

Electricity is produced by the burning of fossil fuels in **thermal power stations**. The electricity produced is then be distributed to users, often through a national network or grid. The fuel used in these power stations is bulky and costly to transport, so power stations are generally built quite close to the source of the raw material. Over time, however, a country may begin to rely on imported fossil fuels (or have few in the first place), and so this factor becomes less important. There is a considerable safety issue with the siting of nuclear power stations, which are consequently located away from major centres of population. The generation of electricity from HEP sources is determined by the location of the water supply, which is often in mountainous regions away from centres of population.

Check this!…

1 Why do you think many countries rely on oil and gas for their energy supplies?

2 Why is nuclear energy such a controversial issue?

3 What problems are caused by the use of wood for fuel?

Renewable energy resources

Figure 10.3 The advantages and disadvantages of renewable resources

Hydro-electric power (HEP)

Hydro-electricity comprises the highest proportion of the renewable types of energy. Although it accounts for only 6.5 per cent of the world's total commercial energy (Figure 10.1a), in many countries it accounts for over 80 per cent (e.g. Paraguay 100 per cent, Norway 96 per cent and Brazil 86 per cent). It is important to both MEDCs and LEDCs – but they must have a constant supply of fast-flowing water. Hydro-electricity can be generated at a natural waterfall (e.g. Niagara Falls), by building a dam across a valley (e.g. the Three Gorges Dam on the Yangtze in China and at Itaipù in Brazil) or where water flows rapidly down a hillside (e.g. Norway).

Advantages
- HEP is renewable.
- It is often produced in highland areas where the population is sparse.
- It is a relatively cheap form of electricity and creates only limited pollution.
- Where dams are built to store water for HEP, they reduce the risks of flooding and water shortages.

Disadvantages
- Dams are very expensive to build.
- Large areas of farmland and wildlife habitats may have to be flooded, forcing people and animals to move.
- Unsightly pylons can cause visual pollution.
- There is always the risk that a dam may collapse.
- Silt, previously spread over farmland, will be deposited in the lake.
- If an area is flooded, the decaying vegetation can release methane and carbon dioxide – two greenhouse gases.

Geothermal energy

Geothermal means 'heat from the Earth'. Heat is stored in some types of rock (magma) beneath the Earth's surface. In volcanic areas, e.g. New Zealand, Iceland, Japan and central America, the heated rocks are near to the surface. In a natural geothermal system, water (usually originating as rain) seeps downwards through cracks and cavities. Where it comes into contact with heated rock, it is warmed and rises to the surface where it is ejected as geysers, hot springs or steam. In some areas of known heated rock, cold water is artificially pumped downwards through boreholes before returning to the surface, usually as steam which can be used to create electricity.

Advantages
- It is renewable.
- It provides a constant supply of heat energy.
- It is relatively pollution free.

Disadvantages
- Electricity generators are expensive to construct and maintain.
- It is limited to volcanic areas.
- There is a risk of eruptions and earthquakes, and the emission of sulphuric gas (a pollutant).

Solar energy

Estimates suggest that the annual amount of energy received from the sun is 7000 times greater than the world's current demand for energy. Solar energy can be used to generate electricity through solar panels and photo-voltaic cells.

Advantages
- Solar energy is safe, pollution free, efficient and limitless in supply.
- There is great potential from solar energy in LEDCs, many of which are in regions that experience many hours of sunshine.

Disadvantages
- Technology has yet to find a cheap and efficient way of constructing solar 'stations'. However, several large transnational companies are trying to do just that.

Back to …

The New Wider World **p294** for information on the Three Gorges Dam; **p122** for a case study of Itaipù in Brazil.

Back to …

The New Wider World **p122** Figure 8.10 which shows the factors involved in the location of an HEP station.

Back to …

The New Wider World **p123** for a case study of geothermal energy in New Zealand.

Biomass

Fermenting dung gives off methane gas which can be used as a source of energy in some LEDCs instead of fuelwood. Although this energy is cheap to produce, it means the dung can no longer be used as a fertiliser, while methane is a greenhouse gas. Some crops, like sugar cane, contain starch which, if fermented, produces a fuel that can be used to power cars (e.g. in Brazil).

Wind energy

Wind turbines (Figure 10.4) need to be located in areas with high and regular wind speeds. Such places are usually found on exposed coasts or upland areas (Figure 10.4).

Advantages
- It is safe (does not give off radioactive emissions) and clean (does not give off chemical emissions). Unlike fossil fuels, it does not contribute to global warming or acid rain.
- It has a minimal effect on local ecosystems.
- After the initial expense of building a wind farm, the production of electricity is relatively cheap.
- Wind farms are likely to be built off-shore in the future.

Disadvantages
- Wind does not blow all the time. At present electricity generated during storms cannot be stored for use during calm periods.
- Groups of 30 metre tall turbines spoil the scenic attraction of the countryside and can affect wildlife, especially birds.
- Currently it is an expensive and not very efficient form of energy. Around 7000 turbines are needed to produce the same amount of electricity as one nuclear power station.

Check this!...

1 Why do you think hydro-electric power is the most commonly used form of renewable energy?

2 Name two advantages and two disadvantages of wind energy.

3 Why does solar energy have such great potential?

Figure 10.4 A wind farm in California, USA

2 What are the factors that influence the development and siting of different types of power stations?

Electricity is produced by the burning of fossil fuels in **thermal power stations**. The electricity produced is then distributed to users, often through a national network or grid. The fuel used in these power stations is bulky and costly to transport, so power stations are generally built quite close to the source of the raw material. Over time, however, a country may begin to rely on imported fossil fuels (or have few in the first place), and so this factor becomes less important. There is a considerable safety issue with the siting of nuclear power stations, which are consequently located away from major centres of population. The generation of electricity from HEP sources is determined by the location of the water supply, which is often in mountainous regions away from centres of population.

Check this!...

1 What is a thermal power station?

2 Why are these power stations usually built close to the source of raw material?

3 Why is the location of nuclear power stations different from those using other fuels?

3 What are the uses, provision and competition for water resources and the impacts of water shortages?

Although there is more water than land on the Earth, 97 per cent of the total is found in seas and oceans and 2 per cent is stored as ice and snow. The remaining 1 per cent is constantly recycled in the hydrological (or water) cycle. As water is neither added to nor lost from the hydrological cycle, the amount of fresh water available for life on Earth remains constant, and it should be a renewable resource.

Over the last 300 years the world's population has increased sevenfold. However, the demand for water for domestic, agricultural and industrial use has increased by 35 times. This increased use of water has been accompanied by an increase in its pollution. The UN estimates that each day 25 000 people die from using contaminated water. Fresh water is also very unevenly distributed. These two factors mean that about 80 countries (40 per cent of the total) and 1.5 billion people are already experiencing 'severe water stress' either within particular regions or at certain times of the year. The UN estimates that by 2050, two-thirds of the world's population (up to 5 million) are likely to be short of reliable, clean water. Most of these people live in LEDCs in Africa, Asia and Latin America.

Back to ...

The New Wider World **p278**
Figure 17.3 for a diagram
of the hydrological cycle.

Reliability of rainfall

Regular water supply in many parts of the world is related to the reliability of rainfall. Many countries experience a pronounced wet and dry season. If the rains fail during one year, the result for crops, animals and sometimes people, can be disastrous. The most vulnerable areas are desert margins and tropical interiors, where average annual amounts are low and the rainy season is short. Here, where a small variation of 10 per cent below the average total can be critical, many countries experience a variation of over 30 per cent (Figure 10.5).

When the rain does fall, it often comes in torrential downpours which give insufficient time for it to sink (infiltrate) into the ground. Instead, surface runoff causes flash floods and water is lost to the local community. Few LEDCs have the money or the technology to build dams to store water. Where they have been built, it has been with

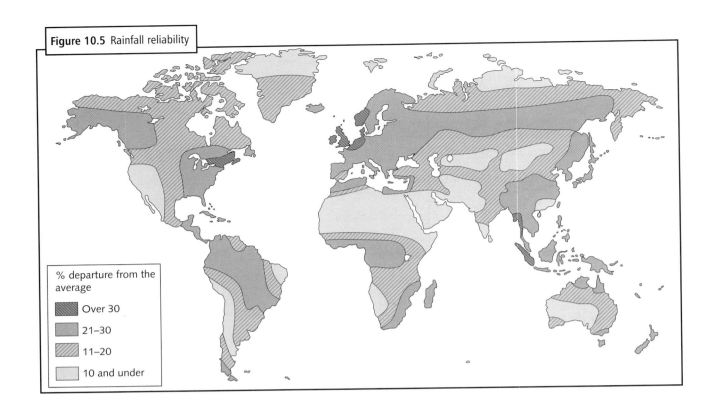

Figure 10.5 Rainfall reliability

% departure from the average

- Over 30
- 21–30
- 11–20
- 10 and under

foreign financial 'aid' which has put the recipient country further into debt. Relatively few places, especially in rural areas, have piped water, and the daily walk to the local well or river can be a distance of several kilometres, taking several hours.

Clean water

The UN estimates that 1500 million people lack a satisfactory or safe water supply. People generally do not take enough care of this essential resource. In LEDCs, water supplies may be contaminated. Water that is dirty or polluted is no longer a renewable resource and often leads to outbreaks of diseases such as cholera, typhoid and dysentery.

The UN 'International Drinking Water Supply and Sanitation Decade' was launched in 1980 to provide 'water and sanitation for all by 1990'. This ambitious target was never realised. There was some progress, especially with water supply – 50 per cent of people in rural areas now have an adequate supply compared with only 30 per cent in 1980. But the rapid growth in population and urbanisation meant that 500 million more people lacked sanitation in 2000 than in 1980. Shortage of fresh water supplies on this scale has an adverse effect on a country's potential for development.

The improvements in rural water supplies were mainly due to international charity organisations. Examples include Oxfam, ActionAid and the Intermediate Technology Development Group (ITDG) which are based in the UK, and Weeping Water, the African Well Fund and the

Back to ...

The New Wider World **p225**
Figure 13.35 for a world map showing the percentage of people with access to safe water supplies.

Back to ...

The New Wider World **p151**
for information about the ITDG.

Water Life foundation, which are based in the USA. These aid organisations have helped local communities to introduce appropriate technology. These included self-help schemes such as:

- digging wells to reach permanent underground supplies
- lining the sides of the well with concrete (to prevent seepage) and adding a cover (to reduce evaporation).

Check this!...

1 Why has the provision of water become such an important global issue?

2 Why is the reliability of rainfall important in providing a regular supply of water?

3 What solutions have been attempted to provide clean drinking water to poorer countries?

Case Study

Drought and water supply in the UK

Back to ...

The New Wider World **pp222–223** for the case study of drought and water supply in the UK.

Using your case study

Use this case study to help you answer questions on water resources. You will need to understand that:

- within an MEDC such as the UK there are variations in water supply and demand
- a period of drought may cause severe water shortages in some parts of a country
- in such a situation the use of water resources requires careful management.

Case study links

One section of Unit 2 of the syllabus is called 'The inter-relationship of physical and human geography'. This includes a study of hazards, for example drought. It may be appropriate to use some of the information about drought in the UK, particularly its management, to answer questions in this section.

Update

In the UK the government agency in charge of managing water resources is the Environment Agency. Go to *The NWW Coursemates* website for a link to the Agency's website. Try the links to the sections on 'Water quality' and 'Water resources'.

Learn it!

1 Describe the areas of the United Kingdom that have **a)** a water surplus and **b)** a water deficit.

2 Explain the pattern you have described.

3 Describe how the authorities in the UK coped with the droughts of 1995 and 1996.

4 Do you think the situation was well managed or not? Give reasons for your answer.

a   Look at Figure 10.1, which gives information about global energy production.

    i   What is meant by the term 'fossil fuels'? (1)

    ii   Name any two fossil fuels on Figure 10.1. (2)

    iii   Which form of energy is not produced commercially? Explain why this is the case. (3)

    iv   Why are some people worried about the use of nuclear power to produce energy? (4)

b   Look at Figure 10.6. This shows how energy is produced in Norway, a country in northern Europe.

    i   Describe the information shown on Figure 10.6. (3)

    ii   Describe good locations for the production of hydro-electric power. (5)

    iii   Why are many people pleased when countries like Norway develop renewable sources of energy such as hydro-electric power? You may refer to examples you have studied. (7)

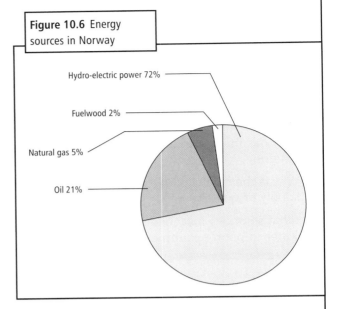

Figure 10.6 Energy sources in Norway

Hydro-electric power 72%

Fuelwood 2%

Natural gas 5%

Oil 21%

EXAM TIPS

You may be able to explain part of your answer by using a sketch or diagram. This may be quicker, and make your point more clearly. In this question, part (b) (ii) asks you to describe good locations for the production of hydro-electric power. You may decide to write about this, but you could draw a diagram instead. If you do this, make sure that you add any notes or relevant explanations to your diagram – but don't repeat everything that your diagram shows, as that just wastes valuable time.

Back to …

The NWW Coursemates website to check your answers to the exam practice question.

⇨ *The New Wider World*, pp111; 118; 121; 184–185; 218–219; 221; 224; 236; 238–240; 254–255; 279; 312

Resource conservation and management

11

1 Why is there a need for sustainable management and the conservation of resources?

The demand for, and the use of, the world's resources continues to grow at an increasingly faster rate. This is mainly due to:

- **population growth** as the number of people in the world continues to increase
- **economic development** as more countries try to develop industrially and economically and attempt to raise their standard of living and quality of life
- **increasing wealth**, especially in more economically developed countries (MEDCs)
- **technological advances.**

How can the Earth's resources be protected?

The combined effects of population growth, economic development, increasing wealth and technological advances means that there is a growing need to manage and protect the Earth's resources. This might be achieved through **sustainable development**. Sustainable development is improving people's standard of living and quality of life without wasting resources or spoiling the environment. It includes:

- conservation, e.g. wildlife and scenery
- recycling, e.g. glass and waste paper
- more efficient use of existing resources
- developing renewable resources, e.g. the wind, waves, tides and the sun
- controlling pollution, e.g. reducing emissions from vehicles, power stations and farm waste
- using **appropriate technology**, e.g. low-cost energy schemes and local building materials.

2 What effects do human activities have upon the natural environment?

Threats to the environment

Global warming

The greenhouse effect
The Earth is warmed during the day by incoming radiation from the sun. The Earth loses heat at night through outgoing infrared radiation. Over a long period, because there is a balance between incoming and outgoing radiation, the Earth's temperatures remain constant.

On cloudy nights, temperatures do not drop as low as on clear nights. This is because the clouds act as a blanket and trap some of the heat. Some of the gases in the atmosphere also act as a blanket, as they prevent the escape of infrared radiation (Figure 11.1). Without these

KEY QUESTIONS

1 Why is there a need for sustainable management and the conservation of resources?

2 What effects do human activities have upon the natural environment?

Key words to know

Sustainable development
Appropriate technology

Back to ...

The New Wider World **p219** Figure 13.20 for a diagram showing the percentages of different greenhouse gases.

greenhouse gases, which include carbon dioxide, the Earth's average temperature would be 33°C lower than it is today. (During the Ice Age, temperatures were only 4°C lower than they are at present.)

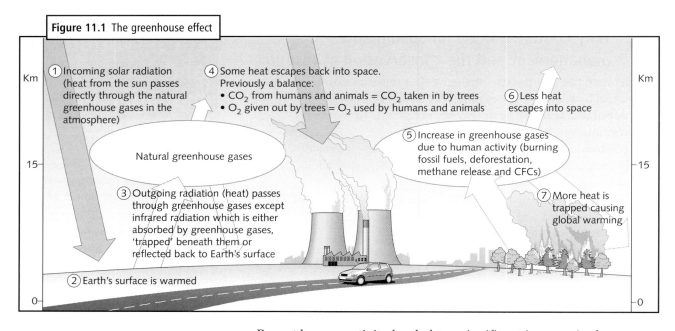

Figure 11.1 The greenhouse effect

① Incoming solar radiation (heat from the sun passes directly through the natural greenhouse gases in the atmosphere)

④ Some heat escapes back into space. Previously a balance:
• CO_2 from humans and animals = CO_2 taken in by trees
• O_2 given out by trees = O_2 used by humans and animals

⑥ Less heat escapes into space

Natural greenhouse gases

⑤ Increase in greenhouse gases due to human activity (burning fossil fuels, deforestation, methane release and CFCs)

③ Outgoing radiation (heat) passes through greenhouse gases except infrared radiation which is either absorbed by greenhouse gases, 'trapped' beneath them or reflected back to Earth's surface

⑦ More heat is trapped causing global warming

② Earth's surface is warmed

Key words to know

Greenhouse gases
Greenhouse effect
Global warming

Recent human activity has led to a significant increase in the amount, and type, of greenhouse gases in the atmosphere. This is preventing heat from escaping into space, and is believed to be responsible for a rise in world temperatures. World temperatures rose by 0.6°C last century (Figure 11.2), with seven of the century's warmest years occurring in the 1990s. A UN report in 2001 suggested, from the use of computer-generated models, that a further rise of 5.8°C could take place before the end of this century. The process by which world temperatures are rising is known as **global warming**.

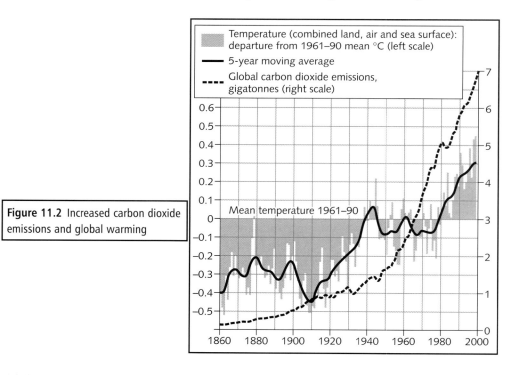

Figure 11.2 Increased carbon dioxide emissions and global warming

Temperature (combined land, air and sea surface): departure from 1961–90 mean °C (left scale)
— 5-year moving average
---- Global carbon dioxide emissions, gigatonnes (right scale)

Mean temperature 1961–90

Causes of global warming

The major contributors to global warming are carbon dioxide and other pollutants released into the atmosphere.

- Carbon dioxide is the most important single factor in global warming. It is produced by road vehicles and by burning fossil fuels in power stations, in factories and in homes. The MEDCs consume three-quarters of the world's energy, so they are largely responsible for global warming. A secondary source of carbon dioxide is deforestation and the burning of the tropical rainforests.
- CFCs (chlorofluorocarbons) from aerosols, air conditioners, foam packaging and refrigerators are the most damaging of the greenhouse gases.
- Methane is released from decaying organic matter such as peat bogs, swamps, landfill sites, animal dung and farms (e.g. ricefields in South-east Asia).
- Nitrous oxide is emitted from car exhausts, power stations and agricultural fertilisers.

Back to ...

The New Wider World
pp236–237 and **p107** of this
Coursemate for information
about the effects of
deforestation.

Effects of global warming

The Intergovernmental Panel on Climatic Change (IPCC), which reported on behalf of the UN in 2001, described some effects that have already been observed. It also predicted other effects that are likely to occur (Figure 11.3):

- As sea temperatures rise, water in the oceans is expanding, causing sea-levels to rise. IPCC scientists claim that sea-level rose by 0.2 metres during the last century. They give an average predicted rise of 0.4 metres for this century.
- Icecaps and glaciers are already melting at a rate never recorded before. Since 1960, sea-ice in the Arctic has retreated by 15 per cent and it is 40 per cent less thick.

Figure 11.3 Some predicted effects of global warming

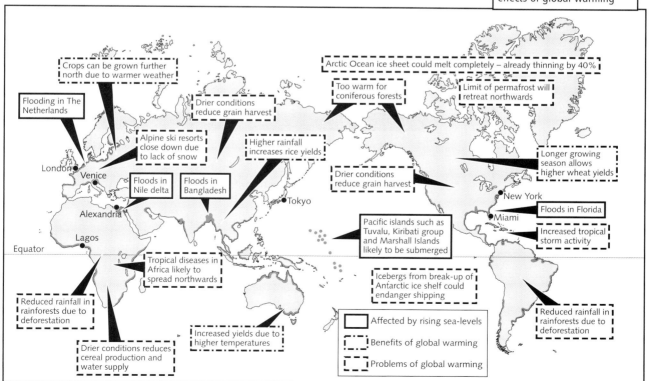

Back to ...

The New Wider World **p312**
for information about
flooding in Bangladesh.

Back to ...

The New Wider World **p224**
and **pp97–99** of this
Coursemate for information
about global water
shortages.

Back to ...

The New Wider World **p111**
and **pp73–76** of this *Coursemate*
for information about the
impact of falling crop yields.

- The release of water currently held in storage as ice and snow in the hydrological cycle could raise the world's sea-level by a further 5 metres. Even a rise of 1 metre could flood 25 per cent of Bangladesh, 30 per cent of Egypt's arable land, and totally submerge several low-lying islands in the Indian and Pacific Oceans (Figure 11.3). At present, 40 per cent of the world's population live within 100 km of the coast – many people are vulnerable to rising sea-levels and storm surges.
- The distribution of precipitation is predicted to change. The IPCC's computer models indicate that places with:
  - sufficient rainfall are likely to get more, resulting in increased flooding (e.g. in northern Europe) – this prediction was made before the disastrous floods that affected the Elbe and Danube basins in 2002
  - insufficient rainfall are likely to get less in terms of both amount and reliability, giving increased drought (e.g. much of Africa) – this prediction claims that the 1.7 billion people (one-third of the world's population) already short of water in 2000 could become 5 billion by 2025.
- Ecosystems may be subject to such a rapid change that plants and wildlife may not have the time in which to adjust. This includes coral reefs, mangrove swamps, wetlands, coniferous and tropical forests, and tropical grassland. Already, trees are coming into leaf, insects are emerging and birds are laying their eggs much earlier in the year.
- Crop yields are expected to fall even further in Africa, as well as in parts of Asia and Latin America, although they may increase in northern Europe and North America.
- A greater proportion of the world's population will be at risk from insect-borne (e.g. malaria and dengue fever) and water-borne (e.g. cholera) diseases.

Throughout the IPCC report, one prediction was constant: it will be the poor who will be hardest hit. The effects will be greatest in the less economically developed countries (LEDCs) – water and food shortages, diseases and natural disasters. These are places where people can least afford to adapt or are unable to migrate.

Check this!…

1 Explain why there is increasing demand for the Earth's natural resources.

2 In what ways does sustainable development try to deal with this issue?

3 Explain what is meant by the 'greenhouse effect'.

4 Summarise any three effects of global warming.

5 Do you think the negative impacts of global warming will be more important than the positive ones? Explain your answer.

Pollution

There are several types of pollution. These include water, noise, visual and air pollution, smog, acid rain, the greenhouse effect, and 'holes' in the ozone layer. Each of these problems has serious implications for human health and well-being and indeed for the whole environment.

Water pollution

For many centuries, people across the world have thought of rivers as being a cheap and convenient method of removing their waste, whether it was domestic, agricultural or, more recently, industrial. It is only recently that governments have reacted to try to improve the quality of water supplies. In the United Kingdom, for example, the government's Environment Agency now has measures in place to reduce the amount of water pollution, the main source of which is leaks from the sewage system. In India, water pollution is a major problem in the River Ganges. There are nearly 700 urban centres on the Ganges, many having inadequate sewage facilities, with the result that waste pours untreated into the river. The government in 1986 invested $270 million in the Ganges Action Plan in an attempt to clean up the river, although this has had limited effects, particularly on industrial pollution.

Noise, visual and air pollution

Noise, visual and air pollution have become serious problems, particularly in large urban centres throughout the world. However, air pollution is the most significant. It is largely caused by the huge increase in car ownership and the number of people who commute to work in cities. In New York, for example, over 2 million people travel into the city centre each day. Large amounts of pollution can cause smog, which reduces visibility and poses a risk to health. In large cities in LEDCs, for example in Rio de Janeiro, such pollution is a major problem. The road system in the city centre is unable to cope with the volume of traffic, which comes to a standstill for many hours in a day. Noise and smog pollution are major problems as a result.

One type of air pollution is the release of particles into the air from burning fuel for energy. Diesel exhaust is a good example of this particulate matter. The particles are very small, and this type of pollution is sometimes referred to as 'black carbon' pollution. The exhaust from burning fuels in cars, homes and industries is a major source of such air pollution.

Another type of air pollution is the release of noxious gases, such as sulphur dioxide, carbon monoxide, nitrogen oxides and chemical vapours. These can involve further chemical reactions once they are in the atmosphere, forming smog and acid rain. This is a serious problem in some cities, e.g. Los Angeles.

Acid rain

Acid rain was first noticed in northern Europe in the 1950s when large numbers of freshwater fish died. Research showed that the water in which these fish had lived contained more than average amounts of acid. Later it was discovered that this extra acid had been carried by rain – hence the term **acid rain.** The acid is formed in the air from sulphur dioxide and nitrogen oxide which are emitted by thermal power stations, industry and motor vehicles (Figure 11.4).

These gases are either:
- carried by prevailing winds across seas and national frontiers to be deposited directly onto the Earth's surface (dry deposition), or
- converted into acids (sulphuric and nitric acid) which then fall to the ground in the rain (wet deposition).

Key words to know

Acid rain

Figure 11.4 Causes and effects of acid rain

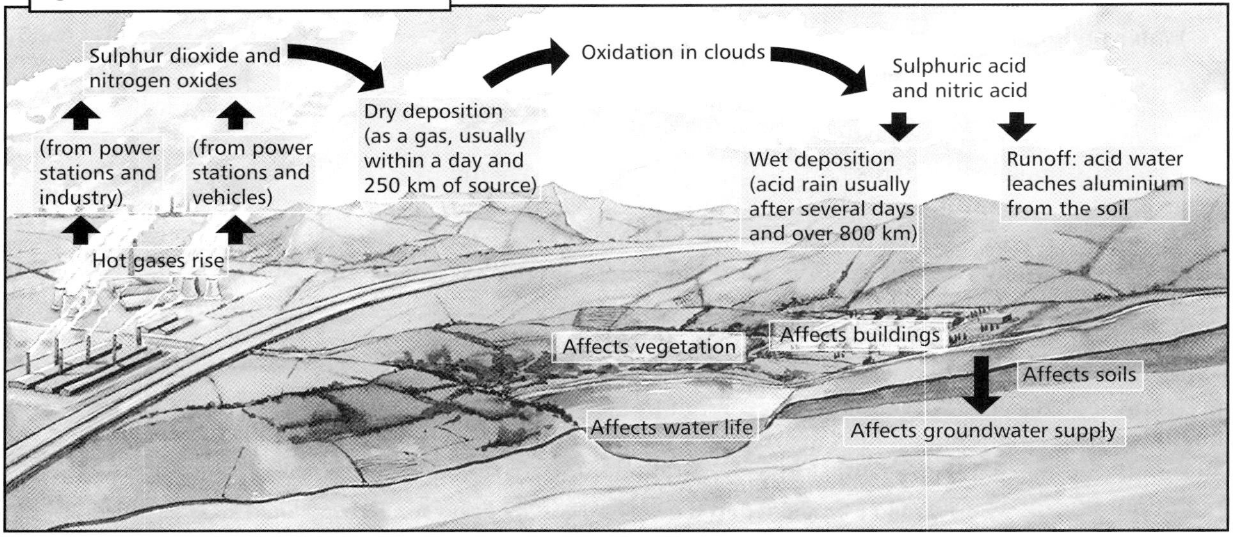

Sulphur dioxide and nitrogen oxides

Oxidation in clouds

Sulphuric acid and nitric acid

(from power stations and industry)

(from power stations and vehicles)

Dry deposition (as a gas, usually within a day and 250 km of source)

Wet deposition (acid rain usually after several days and over 800 km)

Runoff: acid water leaches aluminium from the soil

Hot gases rise

Affects vegetation

Affects buildings

Affects soils

Affects water life

Affects groundwater supply

Clean rainwater has a pH value of between 5.5 and 6 (pH7 is neutral). Today the pH readings are between 4 and 4.5 through most of north-west Europe.

The effects of acid rain
- The acidity of lakes has increased. Large concentrations kill fish and plant life.
- An increase in the acidity of soils reduces the number of crops that can be grown.
- Forests are being destroyed as important nutrients (calcium and potassium) are washed away (leached). These are replaced by manganese and aluminium which are harmful to root growth. In time, the trees become less resistant to drought, frost and disease, and shed their needles.
- Water supplies are more acidic and this could become a future health hazard. For example, the release of extra aluminium has been linked to Alzheimer's disease.
- Buildings are being eroded by chemical action caused by acid rain. The Acropolis in Athens and the Taj Mahal in India have both deteriorated rapidly in recent years.

Soil erosion and management

It can take up to 400 years for 1 cm of soil to form, and between 3000 and 12 000 years to produce a sufficient depth for farming. At present, only 11 per cent of the Earth's land surface is classified as prime agricultural land.

This land is needed to feed an ever growing world population. So far the increase in population has been matched by increases in food production but the capacity of the soil to produce enough food is being stretched to the limit. The problem is made worse where human activity is actually ruining this essential resource, through erosion or degradation (Figure 11.5).

Soil erosion
Erosion is most rapid in areas:
- where the land is mismanaged

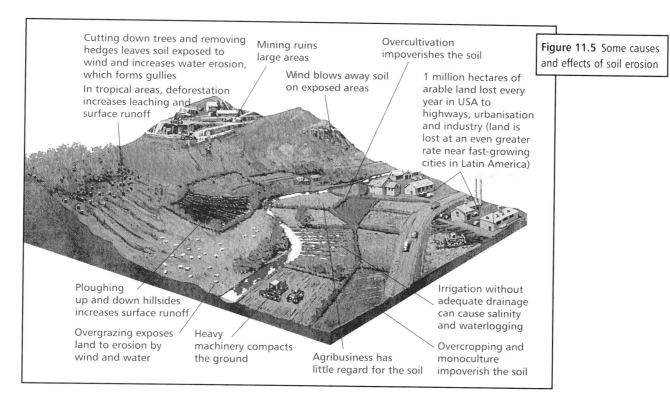

Cutting down trees and removing hedges leaves soil exposed to wind and increases water erosion, which forms gullies

In tropical areas, deforestation increases leaching and surface runoff

Mining ruins large areas

Wind blows away soil on exposed areas

Overcultivation impoverishes the soil

1 million hectares of arable land lost every year in USA to highways, urbanisation and industry (land is lost at an even greater rate near fast-growing cities in Latin America)

Ploughing up and down hillsides increases surface runoff

Overgrazing exposes land to erosion by wind and water

Heavy machinery compacts the ground

Agribusiness has little regard for the soil

Irrigation without adequate drainage can cause salinity and waterlogging

Overcropping and monoculture impoverish the soil

Figure 11.5 Some causes and effects of soil erosion

- where the protective vegetation cover is removed
- where there is rapid population growth
- where the land is steep
- where climatic conditions are extreme, especially if rainfall is seasonal, comes as downpours or is unreliable.

The UN has estimated that an area the size of China and India combined has been lost in the last half-century, and that one-third of the remaining soil could be destroyed by the year 2030.

Removal of vegetation

Most damage to the soil results from the removal of vegetation. **Deforestation** is the major cause. Where vegetation is removed there can be no replacement of humus, no interception of rain by plants and no roots to bind the soil together. The surface is left exposed to rain and wind. If the rainfall occurs as heavy downpours and in areas with steep slopes, the soil will be washed downhill and removed by rivers to leave deep, unusable gullies. If heavy rain falls on more gentle slopes or if the climate is dry and windy, loose material will be removed to leave areas of bare rock. The removal of hedgerows, the ploughing of grassland and the collection of fuelwood all increase the risk of erosion by water and wind.

Overcultivation and overgrazing

Overcultivation occurs when crops are grown on the same piece of land year after year. **Overgrazing** is where there are too many animals for the amount of grass available. Overcultivation and overgrazing tend to occur mainly in LEDCs where the increase in population means that the land is in constant use. Local farmers neither have the money to buy fertiliser for their the land, nor the time to allow a resting (fallow) period for the soil to recover naturally.

Soil management

Soil is a sustainable resource, but only if it is carefully managed. Soil

Back to ...

The New Wider World **p108** for how the removal of hedgerows can contribute to soil erosion in the UK; **p121** for the problems caused by the collection of fuelwood; and **p279** for how the interception of rainfall by plants can halt soil erosion.

Key words to know

Deforestation
Overcultivation
Overgrazing

may have taken centuries to form and without careful management it can be lost within days. Under extreme conditions it can be removed in just a few minutes. Some suggested methods of preventing, or at least limiting, soil erosion are shown in Figure 11.6. At the same time it is important to continue to make productive use of the land.

Figure 11.6 Some attempts to reduce and prevent soil erosion

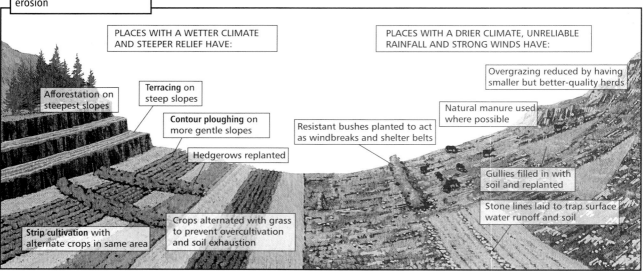

PLACES WITH A WETTER CLIMATE AND STEEPER RELIEF HAVE:

PLACES WITH A DRIER CLIMATE, UNRELIABLE RAINFALL AND STRONG WINDS HAVE:

Afforestation on steepest slopes

Terracing on steep slopes

Contour ploughing on more gentle slopes

Hedgerows replanted

Resistant bushes planted to act as windbreaks and shelter belts

Overgrazing reduced by having smaller but better-quality herds

Natural manure used where possible

Gullies filled in with soil and replanted

Stone lines laid to trap surface water runoff and soil

Strip cultivation with alternate crops in same area

Crops alternated with grass to prevent overcultivation and soil exhaustion

Key words to know

Terracing
Contour farming
Strip farming

Back to ...

The New Wider World **p255** Figure 15.36 for a photograph of rice terraces, and Figure 15.37 for a photograph of contour farming; **p258** Figure 15.45 for a photograph of stone lines.

Various techniques can reduce soil erosion by over 50 per cent (e.g. terracing, the replanting of trees, grass and hedges, contour ploughing and strip cultivation). The addition of mulch and manure also reduces erosion, at the same time increasing soil fertility.

The best protection against soil erosion is to prevent it from being exposed to wind and rain. Trees, bushes and grass can act as windbreaks, improve water retention and bind the soil together. **Terracing** is when artificial 'steps' are cut into steep hillsides and the front of each flat terrace is edged with mud or stone walls. The walls trap water and soil. **Contour farming** is when crops are planted around the hillside rather than up and down the slope. **Strip farming** is when two or more crops are grown in the same field. Sometimes one crop may grow under the shelter of a taller crop – a technique that has been used in Mediterranean areas for a long time. In India, vetier grass, which has deep roots to bind the soil, is being planted in contour strips across hillsides. In drier parts of Africa, stone lines are used to trap surface water runoff and soil. The waste from harvested crops can be used as a mulch. This keeps the ground moist by protecting it from evaporation.

Check this!...

1 How does acid rain form?

2 Explain any two effects of acid rain.

3 How do each of the following contribute to soil erosion?
   a) Removing vegetation
   b) Overcultivation
   c) Overgrazing

4 Explain how careful management may reduce or prevent soil erosion.

Sustainable development – managing the use of resources

Sustainable development should, according to the UN: '… meet the needs of the present without compromising the ability of future generations to meet their own needs.' It should lead to an improvement in people's:

- **quality of life** – allowing them to become more content with their way of life and the environment in which they live
- **standard of living** – enabling them, and future generations, to become better off economically.

This may be achieved in a variety of ways:

- By encouraging economic development at a pace that a country can afford and manage so that the country does not fall into debt.
- By developing technology that is appropriate to the skills, wealth and needs of local people and developing local skills so that they may be handed down to future generations.
- By using natural resources without harming the environment, developing materials that will use fewer resources, and using materials that will last for longer. When using resources, we need to remember the three Rs: *renew, recycle* or *replace*.

Sustainable development needs careful planning. As it involves a commitment to conservation, it also needs the co-operation of different groups of countries through the adoption of global agreements.

Sustainable development in MEDCs

It is often mistakenly believed that the concept of sustainable development cannot be applied to MEDCs. This is not the case. It is the MEDCs that, at present:

- consume most of the world's non-renewable resources, such as fossil fuels, minerals and timber
- are the greatest contributors to global pollution, for example acid rain and the release of greenhouse gases.

Case Study

Sustainable forestry in Malaysia

Back to …

The New Wider World **pp238–240** for the case study of sustainable forestry in Malaysia.

Using your case study

Use this case study to answer questions on resource management. You should understand:

- how interference with the natural ecosystem has caused problems in the Malaysian rainforest
- how forestry management has encouraged more sustainable use of the forests.

Case study links

Section 2.4 of your syllabus, 'The inter-relationship of physical and human geography', considers the impact of people on deserts and tropical rainforests. A major impact of human activity is deforestation, so in answer to some exam questions it may be appropriate to include information about how the Malaysian rainforests were cleared before there was more effective management of the industry.

Update

Go to *The NWW Coursemates* website for a link to the Malaysian Forestry department, which provides information on many aspects of forestry in the country.

Learn it!

1 Describe the distribution of natural rainforest in Malaysia.

2 What is meant by 'secondary rainforest'?

3 Why did deforestation take place in Malaysia? What do think are the similarities and differences between what happened in Malaysia and Brazil?

4 Describe the attempts to make forestry more sustainable in Malaysia.

EXAM PRACTICE

a Look at Figure 11.2. This shows the relationship between carbon dioxide in the atmosphere, and temperature.

   i   What is meant by the term 'global warming'? (1)

   ii Describe the relationship between carbon dioxide emissions and global temperature between 1860 and 2000. (2)

   iii Do you think the graph provides definite proof that global warming is due to the increase in carbon dioxide in the atmosphere? (3)

   iv What are some of the positive and negative effects of a global increase in temperature? (4)

b What is meant by each of these terms:

   i   urban sprawl

   ii overcultivation

   iii desertification? (3)

c i   Many parts of the world have been deforested. Why is it important to reduce the amount of deforestation that is taking place? (5)

   ii With reference to examples, how can the conservation and protection of natural environments be achieved? (7)

EXAM TIPS

You need to read questions carefully to make sure you know exactly what they are looking for. Question (a) (iii) is not exactly a 'catch', but when a question asks 'Do you think the graph provides definite proof?', the answer is unlikely to be 'yes'! Even if you think it is, make sure you give clear and full reasons. Also, read the last questions carefully. Question (c) (i) is specifically about deforestation. However, the final question (c) (ii) gives you the opportunity to write about the conservation and protection of any natural environment, not just rainforests. If you have time (and you know enough), you could refer to more than one environment.

Back to ...

The NWW Coursemates website to check your answers to the exam practice question.

12 Skills

1 Map skills

1 Map skills
2 Interpreting photographs and observing landscapes
3 Graphical skills
4 Looking for patterns

Map scales

All maps should include a scale. This shows how distance on the map (in cm or mm) relates to real-life distance on the ground.

On a map, scale is shown in two ways (see Figure 12.1). Whenever you use a map you should try to use the scale to get an idea of the real-life distance between places.

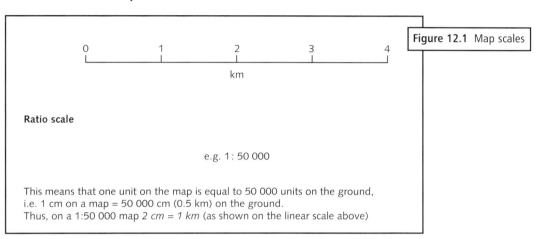

Figure 12.1 Map scales

Ratio scale

e.g. 1: 50 000

This means that one unit on the map is equal to 50 000 units on the ground, i.e. 1 cm on a map = 50 000 cm (0.5 km) on the ground.
Thus, on a 1:50 000 map *2 cm = 1 km* (as shown on the linear scale above)

There are many different scales of map. The larger the scale (e.g. 1:10 000), the more detail is shown; the smaller the scale (e.g. 1:1 000 000), the less detail is shown. Large-scale maps can show road layouts in towns, individual buildings and fields. Small-scale maps, like country maps in atlases, cover huge areas but give very little fine detail.

At GCSE level you are required to be able to read and interpret Ordnance Survey (OS) maps at the 1:50 000 (2 cm = 1 km) scale.

Back to ...

This *Coursemate* **pp123–124** for an example of a 1:25 000 OS map; *The New Wider World* **pp41, 292 and 320** for examples of 1:50 000 OS maps.

Ordnance Survey map symbols

Maps contain a huge amount of information. This is made possible by using symbols instead of written labels, which would take up far too much space. Many symbols are clear in their meaning but they are always explained in a key. The key is usually found at the base or to the side of a map.

Back to ...

The New Wider World **inside back cover** to see a copy of the 1:50 000 OS map key.

Finding grid references

Ordnance Survey (OS) maps have gridlines drawn on them to enable locations to be given. The lines that run 'up and down' and increase in value from left to right (west to east), are called **eastings**. Those that

Key words to know

Eastings
Northings
Four-figure grid reference
Six-figure grid reference

Back to ...

The New Wider World **p41** Figure 3.18: find the village of Thorngumbald. Most of the village is in grid square 2026.

The New Wider World **p41** Figure 3.18: locate the Post Office (P) in the village of Thorngumbald. Its six-figure grid reference is 208266. Notice how the eastings value is represented by the three digits 208 and the northings value is represented by the digits 266. It is the third digit of each set that is the 'tenths' value. Thus, the eastings value is 20 and 8/10ths and the northings value is 26 and 6/10ths.

The New Wider World **p41** Figure 3.18. When answering an exam question, be sure to express a compass direction carefully and precisely. For example, on this OS map Thorngumbald is to the south-east of Hedon, and Hedon is to the east of Salt End.

run across the map and increase in value from bottom to top (south to north), are called **northings**.

To locate a grid square on a map, we use a **four-figure grid reference**. The first two digits refer to the easting value and the second two digits to the northing value.

To locate a point rather than a grid square, each grid square is split into 'tenths' to give a **six-figure grid reference**.

When giving a grid reference it is perfectly reasonable to estimate the 'tenths' but you can always use a ruler to be more precise. Exam mark schemes often allow one-tenth either side.

Giving compass directions

Figure 12.2 shows the compass directions. Usually on a map the direction north is 'straight up', but it is very important that you check the key when examining maps and diagrams. This is why it is also good practice to include a north point on all maps and diagrams that you draw.

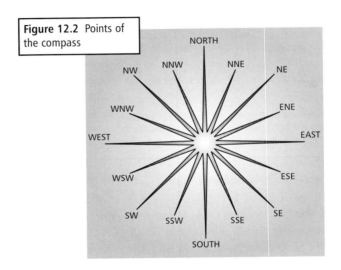

Figure 12.2 Points of the compass

Measuring distances

Every map should have a scale, usually in the form of a measured line (called a *linear scale*) with distances written alongside. To calculate a straight-line distance, you simply measure the distance on the map between the two points in question, using a ruler or the straight edge of a piece of paper. You then line up your ruler or paper alongside the linear scale to discover the actual distance on the ground in kilometres or miles.

A curved distance takes rather longer to work out. The best technique is to use the straight edge of a piece of paper to mark off sections of the curved line, effectively converting the curved distance into a straight-line distance. Look at Figure 12.3 to see how this technique works.

Remember to always give the units, for example kilometres, when writing your answer.

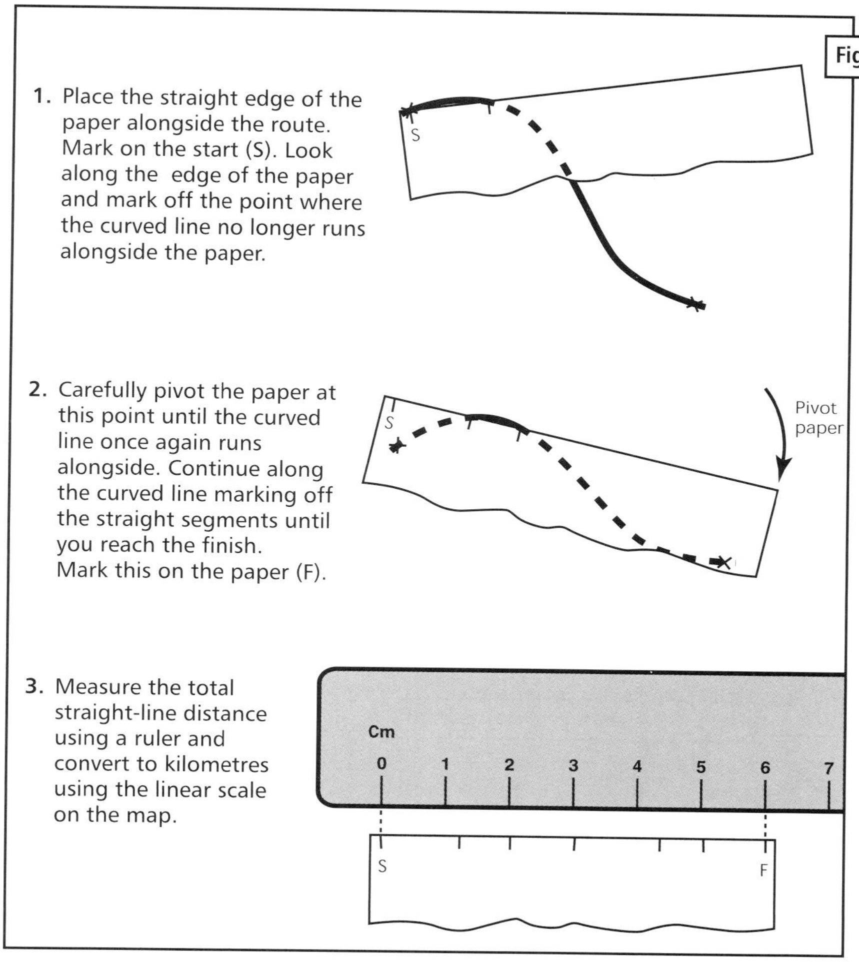

Figure 12.3 Measuring a curved distance

1. Place the straight edge of the paper alongside the route. Mark on the start (S). Look along the edge of the paper and mark off the point where the curved line no longer runs alongside the paper.

2. Carefully pivot the paper at this point until the curved line once again runs alongside. Continue along the curved line marking off the straight segments until you reach the finish. Mark this on the paper (F).

Pivot paper

3. Measure the total straight-line distance using a ruler and convert to kilometres using the linear scale on the map.

Cm

0 1 2 3 4 5 6 7

S   F

Drawing sketch maps

A **sketch map** is a simplified map that is not drawn absolutely to scale. However, it is important to add a scale even if it is just an approximation.

A sketch map is very useful because the person drawing it can decide what to include and what to leave out. It may be that only information about the physical landscape is needed or, alternatively, just the settlements and roads.

A sketch map can be drawn from any kind of map, including OS maps, maps taken from atlases, or those based on maps seen on the internet.

To draw a sketch map you should follow these steps:

- Start by drawing a frame. Make sure that the shape of the frame matches the shape of the area on the original map. It might be a square or a rectangle. Make your frame bigger or smaller than the original if you want to enlarge or reduce it.
- Now carefully transfer the information that you require from the original map onto your sketch map. You could use grid lines to help you – this is easy if your original map is an OS map – or simply draw one or two major guiding features, such as roads or rivers.
- Once complete, you can use colour and shading if you wish, although black-and-white sketches are often the most successful.

Key words to know

Sketch map

- Label and annotate as required (see below), and don't forget to include an approximate scale, a north point and a title.

Labels and annotations
- **Labels** are often single words identifying, for example, physical features or names of places.
- **Annotations** are usually short sentences giving a description or explanation. They are more detailed and often more useful than labels.

Remember that most of the credit for a sketch map will relate to your labels and annotations, which show your ability to interpret the map.

Key words to know

Labels
Annotations

Key words to know

Cross-section

Drawing a cross-section

A **cross-section** is an imaginary slice through a landscape. It is very useful because it helps you to visualise what a landscape actually looks like.

To draw a cross-section you need a piece of scrap paper, a sharp pencil, a ruler and an eraser. The stages of construction are shown in Figure 12.4.

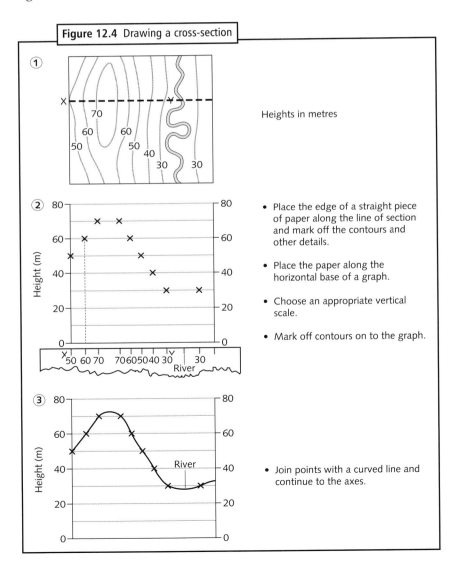

Figure 12.4 Drawing a cross-section

Heights in metres

- Place the edge of a straight piece of paper along the line of section and mark off the contours and other details.
- Place the paper along the horizontal base of a graph.
- Choose an appropriate vertical scale.
- Mark off contours on to the graph.

- Join points with a curved line and continue to the axes.

114

As you complete your cross-section, bear in mind the following points:

- Double-check that you have written down the correct height values.
- Make your vertical scale as realistic as possible – don't exaggerate it so much that you create a totally unreal landscape.
- Complete the cross-section to both vertical axes by carrying on the trend of the landscape.
- Label any features.
- Complete axes labels and give grid references for each end of your cross-section.
- Give your cross-section a title.

A *long profile* is very similar to a cross-section, although it usually involves marking off contour values along a curved distance (see 'Measuring distances' on pages 112–113). Long profiles are most commonly drawn to show changes down a river valley.

Describing the physical landscape

At IGCSE level you are required to explore the ways that relief is presented on OS maps and to identify major relief features.

Relief is the geographical term used to describe the lie of the land. To gain the most marks in an exam you should comment on:

- The height of the land, using actual figures taken from contours or spot heights to support your points. Using words like 'high' and 'low' is fairly meaningless, without the use of actual figures. Refer to different areas or parts of the map using compass directions to enable you to be precise.
- The slope of the land – is the land flat, or sloping? Which way do the slopes face? Are the slopes gentle or steep? Are there bare cliffs exposed? Again, it is important to give precise supporting information such as grid references, compass directions, etc.
- The presence of features such as valleys, dry valleys, escarpments, etc. Refer to names and use grid references.

Describing the human landscape

Ordnance Survey maps contain a lot of information about aspects of human geography, for example roads, settlements, functions and industry.

- **Roads** Different colours are used to show the various types of road. When describing road networks, refer to the type of road and use road numbers whenever possible. For example, the main road passing through Thorngumbald (2026) is the A1033. Use compass directions when describing the pattern of roads. Look out for roads that might be intended to act as by-passes, such as the A1033 to the south of Hedon. Road networks are clearly visible in settlements and it is possible to identify patterns. Notice how in grid square 1430 the roads tend to form a regular grid pattern, suggesting that they are probably part of an older terraced housing area. A more modern housing area, with curved roads and cul-de-sacs, can be found in grid square 1432.

Key word to know

Relief

Back to ...

The New Wider World **p41**
Figure 3.18: study the roads, settlements, functions and industry.

- **Settlements** The pale pink/brown colour on the map shows the extent of the built-up areas. This is where the houses and shops are. The white spaces in between are areas of open ground, such as parks. Some important buildings such as schools – you can see several of these on the outskirts of Hull – are shown separately. The shapes of settlements (for example, whether they are nucleated or linear) can be readily identified.
- **Functions** There are several functions and services shown on the map. In Preston just to the north of Hedon, there is a Post Office, a public house, several places of worship, a school and a sports centre. The number and type of functions can be used to suggest a settlement hierarchy, though it is important to remember that not all functions, particularly shops, are shown on OS maps.
- **Industry** Industrial buildings are usually large and are often arranged in a regular pattern. A good example is the Works to the south of Salt End in grid squares 1627 and 1628. Notice how, in common with many industrial sites, this is on the outskirts of the main town where there is plenty of relatively cheap land available. It has easy access to main roads and, in this case, has a jetty into the river. You can see other industrial buildings alongside the A1033 to the west of Salt End.

Describing patterns on specialist maps

Back to …

The New Wider World **pp205–206** Figures 12.13, 12.15 and 12.16 which are all examples of weather maps.

In addition to OS maps, there are many specialist maps, e.g. geological maps, weather maps, etc.
- Geological maps show the different types of rock below the ground surface.
- Soil maps show different types of soil.
- Weather maps (synoptic charts) show weather information.

To interpret specialist maps you should make good use of the key, which will tell you the meaning of the symbols. In describing what the maps show, apply all the principles of good practice described above. Refer to specific locations, give facts and figures, refer to distances and compass directions, etc. You may be asked to relate a specialist map to an OS map.

2 Interpreting photographs and observing landscapes

Interpreting ground photographs

Back to …

The New Wider World **p150** Figures 9.33–9.34, which show some features of recycling and appropriate technology in LEDCs. In an exam, you could be asked to describe in detail what the people are doing.

Ground photographs are photographs taken by someone standing on the ground. They show what a place looks like as we would see it if we were standing on the ground.

To interpret a ground photograph you need to look at it closely and look for clues to help you understand what is happening. For example, if trees are in leaf and people are wearing shorts then it was probably taken in the summer.

Interpreting aerial photographs

Aerial photographs give us much the same view of an area as we would see when looking out of an aeroplane window. Vertical aerial photographs look directly down on an area much as a map does. Oblique aerial photographs look down at an area at an angle.

Aerial photographs are excellent in showing what an area looks like. They can help us understand and bring to life the detail shown on a map.

You may well be required to relate an aerial photograph to a map extract. Usually you will be asked to work out which way the photograph is looking. To do this, you first need to locate on the map extract some of the features shown at the bottom, middle and top of the photograph. This gives you a line of sight. Then use the compass directions on the map to help you work out which way the photograph is looking.

Interpreting satellite photographs and images

Satellites can provide us with very accurate and detailed photographs often covering large areas of the Earth's surface. Many modern maps are produced using satellite photographs because they are so accurate and up to date.

Computers can create satellite images that use false colours to help identify features of interest, for example green crops, surface water or settlements.

Drawing a sketch from a photograph

It is important to realise that the purpose of a **sketch** is to identify the main geographical characteristics of the landscape. It is not necessary to produce a brilliant artistic drawing; clarity and accuracy are all that is needed. The majority of marks awarded in an exam are given for accurate labels and annotations.

To draw a sketch, you first need to draw a frame to the same general shape of the photograph. Then draw one or two major lines that will subsequently act as guidelines for the rest of your sketch. You could draw the profile of a slope or a hilltop, or a road or river, for example. Consider what it is that you are trying to show and concentrate on these aspects; it may be river features or the pattern of settlements. Don't take time drawing a lot of detail that is not required and only serves to confuse.

Always use a good sharp pencil and don't be afraid to rub things out as you go along.

Finally, remember to label or annotate (detailed labels) your sketch to identify the features, and give your sketch a title.

Figure 12.6 is an annotated sketch of a photograph of a river meander (Figure 12.5).

Back to ...

The New Wider World **p88**
Figure 5.26, which is an oblique aerial photograph of the new town Barra di Tijuca near Rio de Janeiro in Brazil. It shows the layout of the settlement, with the shopping malls and car parks in the foreground, the high-rise apartments in the right background and the mountains in the far distance.

Back to ...

The New Wider World **p205**
Figure 12.12 for a satellite image of a passing depression.

Key word to know
Sketch

Figure 12.5 A meander on a river in Northern Ireland

Figure 12.6 An annotated sketch of the meander shown in Figure 12.5

Key words to know

Field sketch

Drawing field sketches

A **field sketch** is a sketch drawn outside (in the field) to show a particular view. Field sketches are often used to show aspects of the physical landscape, for example a waterfall or cliff. However, they can also be used to show features of the human landscape, for example aspects of village architecture or farming land use.

To draw a field sketch, you should follow the guidelines in 'Drawing a sketch from a photograph' on page 117. Decide how large an area you wish to sketch and draw a frame to the appropriate size and shape. Take time to represent the landscape accurately within your frame but avoid the temptation to strive for a work of art! It is the labels and annotations that are most valuable.

3 Graphical skills

Drawing line graphs

Back to ...

The New Wider World
p10 Figure 1.10, which is a line graph showing the growth in world population since 1800. Notice that the points have been joined up with a freehand curve, which is usually the case with such graphs.

A **line graph** shows continuous changes over a period of time, for example stream flow or population change. It is a very common and effective technique to use, but it is important to remember that time, which is shown on the horizontal axis, must have an equal spacing, for example from year to year.

Drawing bar graphs and histograms

Bar graphs and histograms are one of the most common methods used to display statistical information. However, they are not exactly the same.

Key words to know

Line graph
Bar graph

- A **bar graph** or chart is used to show the frequency or amount of a number of different categories, such as types of goods bought from a supermarket. The bars are drawn with a gap between them and they are coloured or shaded differently because they are unconnected (see Figure 12.7).

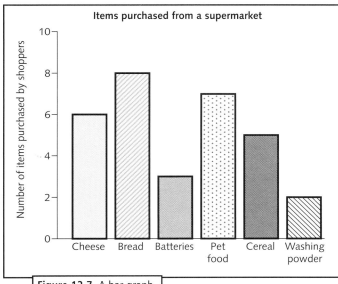

Figure 12.7 A bar graph

Items purchased from a supermarket

(y-axis: Number of items purchased by shoppers, 0 to 10)

(x-axis categories: Cheese, Bread, Batteries, Pet food, Cereal, Washing powder)

Back to ...

The New Wider World **p14**
Figure 1.17 which is a composite bar chart showing the differences between male and female life expectancy in selected countries.

The New Wider World **p164**
Figure 10.15, which is a rainfall climate graph and is an example of a histogram. The monthly rainfall values form part of the total annual rainfall, so they can be drawn as 'touching' bars.

- A **histogram** also uses blocks but with no gaps between them. This is because a histogram is drawn when there is continuous data (such as daily rainfall values over a period of a month) or the values are all part of a single survey, for example the sizes of particles in a sediment sample. As the bars are effectively connected, a single colour or type of shading is used.

It is possible to use multiple bar charts and 'split' or composite bar charts to show two or more pieces of information at the same time.

Key words to know

Histogram
Pie chart
Triangular graph
Rose diagram
Proportional circle

Drawing pie charts

A **pie chart** is quite simply a circle divided into segments, rather like slicing a cake! It is usually drawn to show the proportions of a total, for example the number of shoppers visiting a supermarket each day during one week. Pie charts work best when they have between 4 and 10 segments; pie charts with only one segment are a waste of time and those with many segments become too confusing.

When drawing a pie chart, remember to convert your values into degrees (for percentages multiply by 3.6).

Back to ...

The New Wider World **p186**
Figure 11.11 which compares types of trade for a number of different countries.

The New Wider World **p93**
Figure 6.4 which shows how employment structure data can be displayed on a triangular graph.

Drawing triangular graphs

A **triangular graph** enables three values to be plotted at the same time to produce a single point. The values take the form of percentages that add up to 100. They are commonly used to show soil texture, employment and types of mass movement.

Drawing rose diagrams

A **rose diagram** shows the orientation of observed data, for example wind direction (Figure 12.8). Bars are drawn from an octagonal central shape to represent the number or frequency of each direction.

Figure 12.8 A wind rose for a weather station

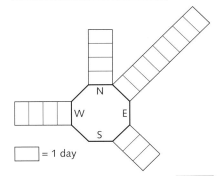

☐ = 1 day

Drawing proportional symbols

Proportional circles are a very effective way to show data, particularly on a base map where spatial variations can be seen. However, they are rather tricky to draw and you will need to choose your scale carefully.

Back to ...

The New Wider World **p93**
Figure 6.3: proportional circles are used very effectively to show regional variations in employment structures in the UK. Notice how the circles are also used as pie charts to show the different types of employment. This complex method of data presentation will score highly in any coursework that you undertake.

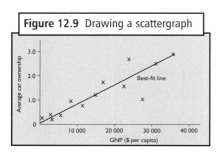

Figure 12.9 Drawing a scattergraph

Key words to know

Scattergraph
Best-fit line
Flow lines
Choropleth map
Isopleth map
Topological map

Back to ...

The New Wider World **p201** Figures 12.3 and 12.4, in which the isotherms have been drawn at 1° intervals.

Select a scale for the radius of your circle. As it is the *area* of the circle that needs to be proportional, you must use the square root value as your radius distance.

Drawing scattergraphs

If you think that two sets of data are related, then the information can be plotted on a graph called a **scattergraph**. To complete a scattergraph you should do the following:

- Draw two graph axes in the normal way, but try to put the variable that is thought to be causing the change in the other (called the *independent variable*) on the horizontal (x) axis. In Figure 12.9, the wealth of a country (GNP) is thought to be responsible for the number of doctors.
- Use each pair of values to plot a single point on the graph using a cross.
- Use a **best-fit line** to clarify the trend of the points if there is one (see Figure 12.9). Your best-fit line should pass roughly through the centre of the points so that there is approximately the same number of points on either side of the line. Use a ruler to draw a straight line. The best-fit line does *not* need to pass through the origin.

The resultant pattern can now be described.

Drawing flow lines

Flow lines are an excellent way to show movement, for example where people visiting a particular country have come from. Each line is drawn with its width proportional to its value, for example 1 cm = 10 million tourists. Flow lines are most effective when drawn on a base map.

Drawing choropleth maps

A **choropleth map** is a map that uses different colours or density of shading to show the distribution of data categories.

Notice the following key features in Figure 1.2 on p5 of *The New Wider World*:

- The base map shows regions or areas, in this case countries.
- Data is divided into a number of groups or categories. Ideally there should be between four and six categories. Notice that the category values do not overlap.
- The darker the shading, the higher the value.
- The map has a powerful and immediate visual impact; it is an effective form of mapping.

Drawing isopleth maps

An **isopleth map** is a map that uses lines of equal value to show patterns. Contours are a good example of isopleths, and are usually drawn at intervals of 10 metres.

Some of the most common isopleth maps are drawn to show aspects of weather and climate, e.g. isobars show pressure, and isotherms show temperature.

Whilst isopleth maps are rather difficult maps to draw, they are very effective at showing patterns, particularly when they are superimposed on a base map.

To draw an isopleth map, you need to mark your observed data onto a base map or sheet of tracing paper/acetate. You then need to consider how many lines to attempt to draw and at what intervals you will draw them. This decision is largely 'trial and error' and you may need to have a go in rough first.

Look at Figure 12.10 to see how isopleths are drawn. Notice how they pass between values that are higher and lower than the value of the line. Just remember that all values to one side of a line will be higher, and all those to the other side will be lower.

There is a degree of individual determination and decision-making, so do not worry if your map turns out to be slightly different from those of your neighbours.

Drawing topological maps

A **topological map** is a map that is not drawn to a true distance scale. Whilst it shows where places are relative to each other, it often appears distorted.

Figure 12.11 is a topological map which shows the railway network of Northern Ireland. Whilst stations are located correctly according to their position on the various lines, no attempt has been made to draw the map to a true distance scale.

Topological maps can be very effective and can stimulate discussion, such as those drawn to a scale of time taken rather than distance.

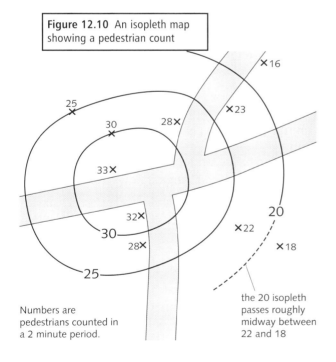

Figure 12.10 An isopleth map showing a pedestrian count

Numbers are pedestrians counted in a 2 minute period.

the 20 isopleth passes roughly midway between 22 and 18

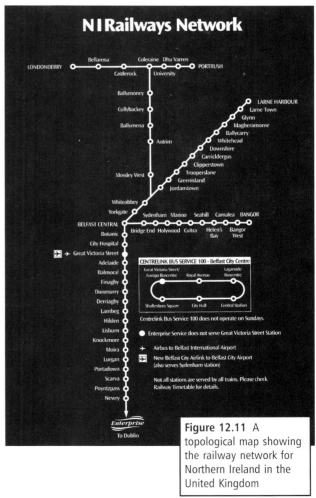

Figure 12.11 A topological map showing the railway network for Northern Ireland in the United Kingdom

4 Looking for patterns

How to 'describe'

To **describe** a map, photograph or diagram you need to put into words what it shows. Start by describing the overall picture or pattern. Refer to the information available on the map, photograph or diagram and give actual facts and figures to support your statements. Then, if appropriate, look for any exceptions (called *anomalies*) to the general pattern. The most important thing is to be as precise and detailed as you can. Also, avoid giving reasons unless you are specifically asked to 'explain'.

How to 'compare' and 'contrast'

To **compare** or **contrast**, you need to write about similarities and differences, for example between two areas on a map. It is essential to make comparisons all the way through your answer, so you should use words like 'whereas' or 'compared with'. Avoid the temptation to write separate paragraphs on the two areas under discussion.

As with making a description, you should refer to places and data wherever possible.

How to 'explain' or 'give reasons'

To **explain** patterns on maps or diagrams you need to try to think of reasons why they exist. This is much more difficult and will test your understanding of geography. You may need to refer to other maps and diagrams to help you. For example, to explain the hydrographs in Figure 17.6 on p280 of *The New Wider World* you could write:

'The main reason why the hydrograph for drainage basin A has a higher peak and more rapidly rising and falling limbs than the hydrograph for drainage basin B is because there is a much higher drainage density in basin A than in B. In basin A, water passes quickly into river channels and then it flows rapidly to the gauging station resulting in a dramatic hydrograph. In basin B, the lower drainage density means that it takes far longer for water to pass through the system hence the longer time lag and the flatter hydrograph.'

You will often be awarded marks for suggesting a reasonable explanation even if it is not absolutely accurate; an examiner will give you credit for making a reasonable suggestion.

How to 'analyse'

An **analysis** is very similar to an explanation except that it usually involves more detail and a much greater use of facts and figures. When conducting your coursework you will probably be required to **analyse** your data.

Key words to know

Describe
Compare and contrast

Back to ...

The New Wider World
pp268–269 Figures 16.20 and 16.22: a comparison between the two volcanic eruptions shown in these photographs might read as follows:

'In Figure 16.20 the volcano is erupting large quantities of red-hot lava, whereas the volcano in Figure 16.22 is erupting dense black clouds of ash and pyroclastics. An ash cloud is rising into the atmosphere from the volcano in Figure 16.22, whereas there is no ash cloud in Figure 16.20. Both eruptions look very dramatic and dangerous.'

Key words to know

Explain
Analyse

Back to ...

The New Wider World **p81** Figure 17.8: an analysis of this complex hydrograph is given in the Case Study box. Notice that it involves a detailed study of the graph together with an interpretation of the effects of drainage basin characteristics on river flow.

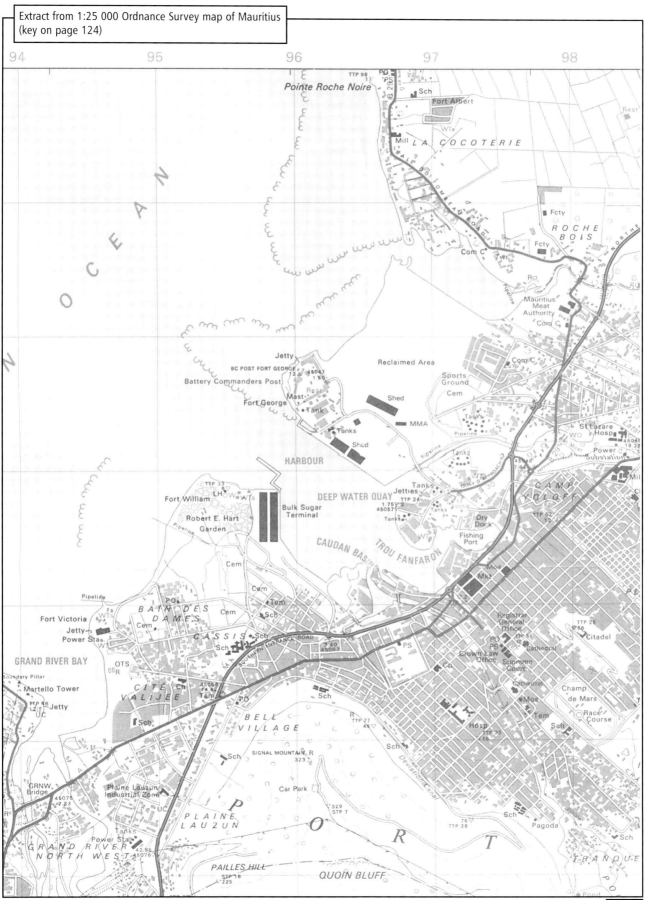

M 1 Bridge ....Motorway

Culvert ....Road – Main A

Embankment ....Road – Main B

Cutting ....Road – Other

....Track

....Footpath

....Cane Track

........................Town or other populated area

..............................Named or Public Building

11KV ....Power Line

R ....Ruin

....Cliff, Rock

....District Boundary

△ ▽ ....Trigonometrical Station – Major, Minor

....Bench Mark

Depression ....Contours (V.I. 10m)

....Sand or Mud

............Watercourse, Waterfall, Rapids, Dam

..........Watercourse (wide), Waterfall, Rapids

OWH OW OS WT ......Waterhole, Well, Spring, Water Tank

....Marsh or Swamp

....Scattered Trees

....Filaos (Casuarina)

....Coral

Scale 1: 25 000

| Metres 1000 | 500 | 0 | 1 kilometre = 0.6214 mile | 1 | 1 Mile =1.6093 kilometres 2 | 3 Kilometres |
| Yards 1000 | 500 | 0 | 1/4 | 1/2 | 3/4 | 1 | 2 Miles |

ABBREVIATIONS

Cem	Cemetery
Ch	Church
Com C	Community Centre
Fcty	Factory
Hosp	Hospital
LH	Lighthouse
Mkt	Market
M	Mill
Mos	Mosque
PS	Police Station
PO	Post Office
Resr	Reservoir
Sch	School
Tem	Temple